Electronic pr~~oject~~

home security

Electronic projects for home security

Owen Bishop

PC Publishing

PC Publishing
4 Brook Street
Tonbridge
Kent TN9 2PJ

First published 1991

© PC Publishing

ISBN 1 870775 12 0

British Library Cataloguing in Publication Data

Bishop, O.N. (Owen Neville)
  Home security projects.
  1. Building. Electronic security equipment.
  Construction – Amateur's manuals
  I. Title
  621.38928

  ISBN 1-870775-12-0

Phototypesetting by Scribe Design, Gillingham, Kent
Printed and bound in Great Britain by BPCC Wheatons Ltd, Exeter

Contents

Introduction

Thanks to electronics, we can now obtain security against intruders, fire, flood and other hazards at low cost, yet with a high degree of reliability. As would-be intruders become more determined and more cunning, electronic measures to outwit them become more sophisticated and effective. A recent survey in the UK has shown that even simple security measures reduce the incidence of crime by about 40%. There is a wide variety of ready-made security devices available in the shops, and whole systems can be bought 'off the shelf'. However, there is much to be said for building your own system. There is not only the saving in cost, but the advantage that the system can be tailored to your own special needs. Moreover you can start with a minimal system — perhaps just a smoke alarm or the protection of single door — and expand it to a full system as your requirements develop. There is also the point that a home-brew system has that element of novelty and surprise that is not found in the commercially available systems. This could be enough to fool or deter a would-be intruder.

This book explains the fundamental principles of home security and how we use electronics to achieve it. The circuits have been made as simple and cheap as possible to build, without compromising their reliability. Their simplicity makes them suitable as beginner's projects. The devices are modular so that they can be used individually as stand-alone devices, or be combined as required into a flexible and comprehensive security system. All the circuits work on batteries and some have such low power requirements that this is the ideal means of powering them. This also has the advantage that the circuits are entirely safe for the beginner to attempt. A circuit for using an inexpensive ready-made mains power supply unit with battery backup is also described.

The circuits are built using stripboard, one of the most popular construction techniques. For those who are new to electronics, the appendix explains how to work with this.

The sample stripboard layout shown here shows the way various stripboard techniques are depicted in the rest of the book. The ⊗ symbol means the copper strip is to be cut. The ●—● symbol means copper strips are to be bridged.

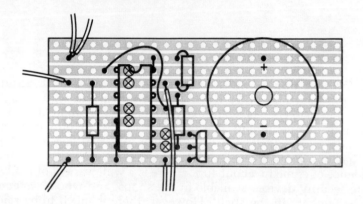

1 Security against intruders

The function of a good security system is to raise the alarm as soon as an intruder attempts to or succeeds in entering the home. Although electronics can do a lot to achieve this, physical protection plays an essential role. By physical protection we mean:

★ strong doors and windows that can not easily be forced open
★ door locks, door chains, and window locks of approved design
★ a household routine that ensures that doors and windows are closed and locked whenever the house is unoccupied, or whenever the occupants are asleep or likely to be inattentive (for example, in the evenings when watching TV)

These elementary precautions would be enough in themselves were it not that there are always skilful operators who can circumvent them. Unless it is lined with sheets of steel, even the stoutest wooden door will succumb to a sledge-hammer. Even the most secure lock is useless if the intruder decides to open the door by detaching its hinges. The most tightly shut window can be penetrated by cutting out the glass. And there is always human error and forgetfulness to result in precautions not being taken on just that very night when the burglar calls. Electronic devices provide that extra level of security and reliability that, taken in conjunction with good physical protection, will make the home virtually unassailable.

Electronic security systems provide us with two lines of defence against intruders:

First line of defence
This usually consists of a loop of wire which runs to switches on all the windows and doors on the premises. This is known as a *peripheral loop*. If an attempt is made to enter the house by any

3

window or door, the alarm sounds. A system based on these principles has the advantage that it prevents the intruder from entering your house and inflicting damage on its contents or, possibly, its occupants. Also there is little likelihood of false alarms being triggered. The main disadvantage is cost, though it is far less expensive if you install it yourself, as described in Chapters 5 to 7.

Second line of defence
This consists of one or more sensors placed at strategic positions in the house. These are usually stand-alone units, each with its own alarm siren, though they can be linked into an integrated system, as explained in Chapter 5. The sensors detect the presence of an intruder in various ways, by detecting:

★ when an infra-red beam is broken (active infra-red sensor)
★ the heat radiated from the body of the intruder (passive infra-red sensor)
★ ultrasound reflected from a moving person or object
★ vibration caused by movement
★ interference with booby-trapped objects

Although it may be possible to position these sensors so that they cover likely points of entry, it more often happens that these devices do not detect the intruder until after the house has been entered and its contents possibly damaged. The advantage of such sensors is that they are usually easily installed. Many types can be purchased ready to fix to the wall. Also it is easy to add new sensors as required, so there need be no initial installation cost. However, these devices which rely on remote sensing have one inherent weak point. The more sensitive the device, the better it is at detecting an intruder. But the more sensitive the device, the more likely it is to be triggered accidentally. Depending on the type of sensor, the noise of passing traffic, the flapping of curtains at an open window, a flash of lightning, or a heavy-pawed dog, may result in a false alarm. False alarms are to be avoided at all costs. not only are they a nuisance and inconvenience to the householder and the neighbours, but they amount to 'crying wolf'. A security system that is continually sounding false alarms soon loses credibility. Neighbours hearing the siren sound yet again, express annoyance, but do not bother to investigate or to call the police.

Associated with the sensors intended to detect intruders are those for detecting other hazards. Foremost among these are various devices for giving early warning of fire. Flood is the other major hazard; adequate warning of an overflowing roof tank may prevent costly damage to the rooms below. A temperature sensor in the deep-freezer can warn when the appliance has accidentally been switched off or has developed some other fault. Sensors of these types as well as those designed for detecting intruders are described in Chapters 2 to 4.

Physical and electronic protection against intruders are backed up by *psychological protection*. One aspect of psychological protection is *deterrence*. Few intruders would deliberately try to break into a well-protected home, if there was another poorly protected or unprotected home a few streets away. It therefore makes sense to advertise the fact that you have a security system in operation. One good advertisement is a siren enclosure mounted prominently on the front of the house even if the enslosure is a dummy with no siren inside it! It is also worth while to exhibit notices stating that the premises are protected. A range of small stick-on labels of this type is available for purchase. Fix these inside windows on the ground floor. They may well save you the hassle of an attempted break-in.

An intruder may also be deterred if it appears that the house is occupied. A device which automatically switches on the light at dusk is a common way of simulating that someone is at home. Many such devices are available from electrical stores. In this book we describe one that is rather more sophisticated so is less likely to be detected by the observant intruder.

Other aspects of psychological protection are *uncertainty* and *surprise*. By definition, an intruder is not on home ground, and therefore is at a psychological disadvantage. This is a weak point. Anything that keeps the intruder guessing presses home that feeling of insecurity. Here the electronics enthusiast has the lead on the person who buys commercially-made protection devices. Those who make a habit of burglary and related activities are usually well aware of the range of devices available and the best ways of countering them. A 'home-brew' system has that element of uncertainty that makes the intruder wonder if it would be better to try elsewhere. A novel type of infra-red detector is bad enough, but when there are booby traps as well, it is time to give up altogether! For this reason, this book includes a number of unusual projects and some booby traps among its armoury of weapons against the intruder.

2 Simple projects for home security

This chapter contains a number of simple stand-alone projects that can be used in various ways to protect the home from intruders. All the alarm circuits described in this chapter switch on the alarm directly. If preferred, the alarm can be switched by a tamper-proof circuit as in Project 11. Some of the projects in this chapter can be incorporated later into the system described in Chapters 5 to 7.

Project 1 Single-door alarm

This circuit sounds an alarm whenever the door is opened. Once triggered, the alarm continues to sound even if the door is closed again. It can·be silenced only by pressing a hidden reset button. Although it is mainly intended as an intruder alarm to set off a loud siren, it can also be used 'keeping watch' in various other ways. For example, it could be used to set off a buzzer when a young child opens the back door and wanders out into the garden.

How it works
Fig 2.1 shows the circuit, which is based on the action of two cross-coupled NAND gates. Connected in this way, the gates form a bistable circuit, or *flip-flop*. Inputs at pins 2 and 13 are normally held at a logic high level. As the name 'bistable' implies, the flip-flop is stable in two states. In its SET state, pin 3 is high and pin 11 is low. The converse applies in the RESET state. Normally, the flip-flop is in its RESET state, and pins 2 and 13 are high. The output at pin 3 is low and no current flows to Q1. Since Q1 is off, no current flows through the *audible warning device* (AWD).

Input at pin 2 is held high because the pin is connected to the positive rail through a normally-closed switch SW2. For protecting

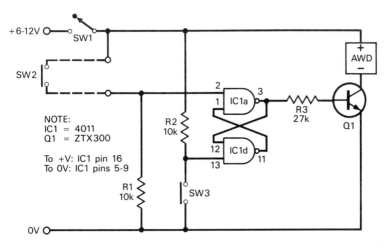

Figure 2.1 Project 1: single door alarm circuit

a door, this switch is usually a reed-switch mounted on or recessed into the door frame (Figs 2.2 and 2.3). A magnet is mounted on or recessed into the door itself so that, when the door is closed, the magnetic field causes the contacts of the reed switch to close together. When the door is opened, the removal of the magnetic field causes the contacts to spring apart. In other words, SW2 is now open. The voltage at pin 2 falls, pulled down by resistor R1, setting the flip-flop, and the output at pin 3 goes high. This turns on Q1, causing a current to flow through the AWD. The alarm is sounded since the alarm is controlled by the flip-flop. It continues to sound even if the door is closed again, closing SW2. To silence the alarm, the flip-flop must be reset. This is done by pressing SW3, to give a brief low input at pin 13. Another way of silencing the alarm is to turn off the power switch SW1, so it is very important that the circuit should be well hidden.

The circuit is proof against tampering by attempts to cut the wire between the door switch and the rest of the circuit. If either of the wires is cut, this has the same effect as opening the switch, and the alarm sounds.

To give maximum security, the main circuit is located at some distance from the door, perhaps concealed in a cupboard or placed on a shelf with other objects in front of it. The AWD or siren may be housed in the same enclosure as the circuit board and battery.

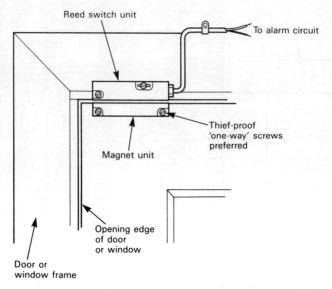

Figure 2.2 Reed switch and magnet suitable for surface mounting

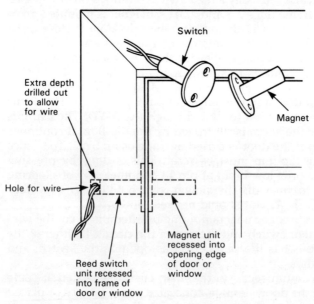

Figure 2.3 Reed switch and magnet suitable for recessing into a wooden framed window or door

Alternatively, the siren can be mounted in the loft or on the front of the house (p. 113).

Construction

The circuit is built on a small piece of stripboard (Fig 2.4) on which there is room for a small solid-state buzzer as the audible warning device. This is suitable if the alarm is to be heard only in one room. To rouse the whole household (and the neighbours as well!) subsititute a solid-state siren. There are a number of low-current sirens available or you can use the alarm circuit described in Project 5. Compared with a buzzer, a low-current siren has the advantage that it is considerably louder and that its note is either intermittent or warbling, so making it more noticeable against the background of the other sounds in the home and street.

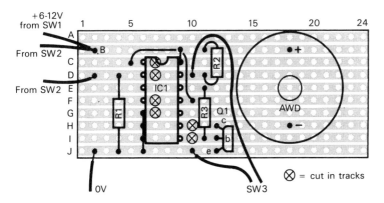

Figure 2.4 Project 1: single door alarm − stripboard layout

If the AWD is not to be mounted on the circuit board or you are installing an external siren, solder terminal pins at B18 and H18 and run wires from these. Solid-state AWDs usually have a positive and a negative terminal so take care to connect the positive terminal to B18 and the negative terminal to H18.

The circuit uses only two of the four gates of IC1. The inputs to the two unused gates are connected to 0V by the solder blob at G6 to J6, and by the uncut copper strips joining pin 6 to pin 9 and pin 7 to pin 8. It is important that these inputs are connected in this way, otherwise the ic as a whole may not function properly.

Figs 2.2 and 2.3 show how to mount the door switch. Notes on wiring techniques are on p. 98.

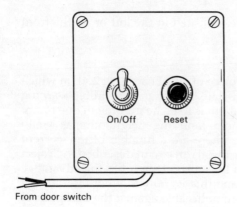

From door switch

Figure 2.5 The completed single door alarm

The circuit operates on any voltage in the range 6V to 12V, provided that this is suitable for the chosen AWD. Since the current required is only 0.6mA when the circuit is quiescent, it can be run from a small 9V alkaline battery (PP3) for several hundred hours. The use of such a small battery means that the housing itself may be small and therefore inconspicuous. The board and battery will fit into a plastic box about 65mm × 60mm × 40mm with S1 and S3 mounted on the lid (Fig 2.5). The circuit board is fitted into slots moulded into the sides of the box. The battery may be held in place by a piece of Blu-tack or a double-sided adhesive pad ('Sticky Fixer').

Before testing the device, make sure that the door is closed. When the device is switched on, the flip-flop may go to the SET state, making the AWD sound immediately. Silence it by pressing S3. Open the door and check that the AWD sounds; check also that it continues to sound if the door is closed, but can be silenced by pressing S3.

Components required
Resistors (see p.139)
R1,R2   10k
R3   27k

Semiconductor
TR1   ZTX300 npn transistor

Integrated circuit
IC1   4011BE quadruple 2-input NAND gate

Miscellaneous
SW1   single-pole single-throw toggle switch
SW2   reed switch and magnet
SW3   push-to-make push-button
stripboard 10 strips by 24 holes
1mm terminal pins (5 off)
suitable plastic enclosure
14-way d.i.l. socket
audible warning device — solid-state buzzer or solid-state low-current siren
battery clip (PP3 type)
6V or 12V battery holder (optional)

Project 2 Broken light-beam alarm

Although the circuit employs a diode sensitive to infra-red radiation, it is intended to work with visible light, either daylight or artificial light. It depends upon the well-known principle of detecting when a beam of light is broken, but with the difference that the circuit is sensitive to rapid changes in the amount of light reaching the diode, but not to slow changes. Thus, if lighting conditions change slowly, as happens at dawn or dusk, or if the sun is gradually obscured by cloud, there is no response. A rapid change, such as that caused by someone passing in front of the sensor, by switching off the lights in the room, or by flashing an electric torch at the sensor, immediately triggers the alarm. Once the alarm is sounding the circuit must be reset to silence it. There are two versions to this circuit, one with a continuously sounding alarm and the other with an intermittent alarm note. The former version is also suitable for connecting into a household system (see p. 95).

How it works
The sensor is an infra-red photodiode (D1, Fig 2.6), which is reverse-biased. In this condition, only a small leakage current passes through the diode, from cathode (k) to anode (a). Under steady lighting conditions, a steady current flows through R1, and there is a constant voltage across it. If the light level falls, the current falls and the voltage drops proportionately.

An operational amplifier wired with a capacitor on its (−) input and a feedback resistor acts as a differentiator. That is to say, its output depends not on the input voltage level but on the *rate of*

11

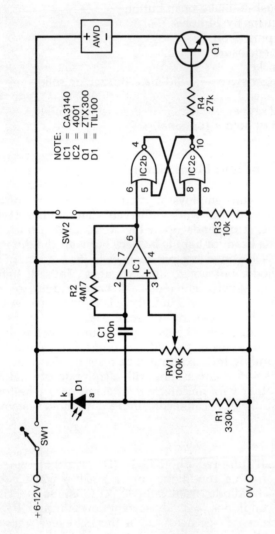

NOTE:
IC1 = CA3140
IC2 = 4001
Q1 = ZTX300
D1 = TIL100

Figure 2.6 Project 2: broken light beam alarm circuit

change of the input. For a constant input, the output is approximately equal to the voltage applied to its (+) input. This voltage is taken from RV1, acting as a potential divider. When operating on a 12V supply, this is set to hold the (+) input at about 4V, so the output of the operational amplifier is also 4V. This counts as a logic 'low'. Since output depends inversely on the change in input, a fall in input voltage leads to a rise in output voltage. The amount of rise depends on the rate of change of input. If there is a *slow* fall in voltage at the (-) input, the output rises slightly. The rise is usually less than a volt, so this still counts as a logic 'low'. However, if there is a *rapid* fall in input voltage, as might be caused by an intruder, the output rises by several volts. This counts as a logic 'high' and triggers the next stage of the circuit.

The next stage is a flip-flop, based on two NOR gates. In contrast to the flip-flop in Project 1, which uses NAND gates, the inputs of this flip-flop are normally held low and a high input pulse is needed to make it change state. The flip-flop is first reset by pressing SW2 to make pin 9 high. Pin 4 becomes high and pin 10 becomes low. No current flows to Q12 and the AWD is off. When the light beam is broken rapidly, the high pulse from IC1 sets the flip-flop and pin 10 goes high. Current flows to Q1, turning it on and making the AWD sound.

Fig 2.7 shows an astable multivibrator (or oscillator) circuit built from the two spare gates of IC2. Adding this to the circuit of Fig 2.6 gives an intermittent alarm sound instead of a continuous one. The circuit of Fig 2.7 oscillates with a frequency of about 1Hz. It is

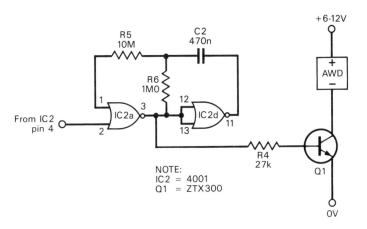

Figure 2.7 Intermittent alarm modification − circuit

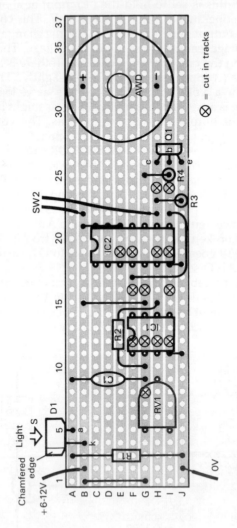

Figure 2.8 Project 2: broken light beam stripboard layout

controlled by the logic level applied to pin 2. If this is high, the output at pin 3 is low, whatever the state of the input at pin 1. This disables the multivibrator and, since pin 3 is low, Q1 is off and there is no sound from the AWD. When pin 2 is made high, by a high level from pin 4 of the flip-flop, the multivibrator is enabled. Pin 3 alternates between high and low. Q1 and the AWD are turned on and off once a second. This gives the intermittent note. An intermittent alarm sound is much more noticeable than a continuous one so, unless you have a special reason to prefer a continuous note, it is better to incorporate the multivibrator as in Fig 2.7.

Construction
Fig 2.8 shows the AWD mounted on the stripboard, but it may be mounted elsewhere, perhaps in another room. The remarks made in Project 1 about locating the AWD apply to this project too. Begin by assembling the diode and the operational amplifier circuit. The anode and cathode terminals of the photodiode are usually distinguished by having a chamfered edge of the package directly above the cathode. The diode is specifically sensitive to infra-red light so works well with sunlight or incandescent lamps. It is less satisfactory with fluorescent lamps. To test this section of the circuit, adjust RV1 so that the voltage at pin 3 of IC1 is about 4V, when using a 12V supply. On a 6V supply, adjust it to 2V. Output (pin 6) is about the same value. Let light from a window or lamp fall on the sensitive face of the photodiode (see Fig 2.8). Monitor the output at pin 6 of IC1; wave your hand in front of the diode and watch the output voltage rise rapidly. Try moving your hand *very slowly* in front of the photodiode; there is only a very slight rise.

Complete the circuit, as in Fig 2.8 or 2.9. Note that in Fig 2.8 the unused NOR gates have their input pins (1, 2, 12, 13) connected to the positive supply. Wire the push-button (SW2) to the board. Check that the AWD is silenced by pressing SW2, but it sounds (either continuously or intermittently) on the slightest rapid movement of your hand in front of D1. RV1 acts as a sensitivity adjustment. The circuit is less sensitive if RV1 is set to a lower voltage, since the output of the amplifier is lower and therefore requires a faster change of input to make it rise to the logic high level.

The circuit operates on any voltage in the range 6V to 12V. It requires 2.4mA quiescent current at 6V or 3mA at 12V, so it is feasible to operate it from a battery, including a 9V PP3 alkaline

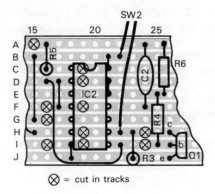

Figure 2.9 Project 2: intermittent alarm modification – board layout

battery. It is housed in a plastic case, with the power switch SW1 mounted on the lid, and a small aperture cut in the side of the case to allow light to fall on the diode. It is preferable for SW2 to be mounted externally, at a distance, and connected to the device by a concealed wire.

Installation
For daylight operation, the device is placed on one side of the room or corridor and receives light from a window on the opposite side. A person passing between the window and the device (or passing outside the window) triggers the alarm. For use at night, a table lamp on the opposite side of the room acts as a source of light. A low-wattage lamp (e.g. 25W) placed 3 or 4 metres away is suitable, though a brighter lamp can be used. In many ways using a room light is better than having a special infra-red lamp, since the table lamp is a common domestic object and will not arouse suspicion. If the intruder turns the lamp off, the alarm sounds. It is usually an easy matter to hide the device on a bookshelf, for example, or to make it inconspicuous in some other way.

Components required
Resistors (see p.139)

R1	330k
R2	4M7
R3	10k
R4	27k
R5	10M (intermittent version only)

| R6 | 1M (intermittent version only) |
| VR1 | 10k miniature horizontal preset |

Capacitors

| C1 | 100n polyester |
| C2 | 470n polyester (intermittent version only) |

Semiconductors

| D1 | TIL100 infra-red photodiode |
| Q | ZTX300 npn transistor |

Integrated circuits

| IC1 | CA3140 CMOS operational amplifier |
| IC2 | 4001B CMOS quadruple 2-input NOR gate |

Miscellaneous

| SW1 | single-pole single-throw toggle switch |
| SW2 | push-to-make push-button |

stripboard 10 strips by 37 holes
1mm terminal pins (4 off)
suitable plastic enclosure
8-way d.i.l. socket
14-way d.i.l. socket
audible warning device — solid-state buzzer of solid-state low-current siren
battery clip (PP3 type) 6V or 12V battery holder (optional)

Project 3 Pressure mat alarm

A pressure mat is a plastic device incorporating two sets of flexible wires, which are pressed together when a weight is applied to the mat. A pressure mat thus acts as a normally-open switch which is closed by a person stepping on the mat. It is usual to conceal the mat and the wiring leading to it beneath the carpet and to position it in a strategic situation, where an intruder is most likely to step on it. A mat is commonly placed just inside a doorway (Fig 2.10) so that anyone entering the room is almost sure to place a foot on it. Or it may protect a particularly valuable object, for example a painting, by being placed where a person reaching for the object is sure to stand.

Pressure mats commonly measure about 75cm by 40cm, but narrower ones are available for placing under stair-carpets. A mat on the stairs is hard to avoid, though it is a good idea to have two

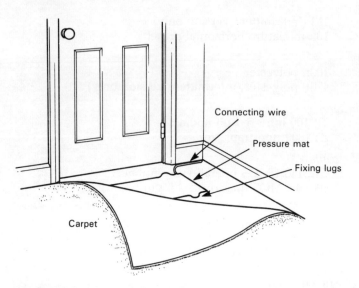

Figure 2.10 Installing a pressure mat

mats on adjacent stairs, in case the intruder is in the habit of ascending two stairs at a time.

Before deciding to install a pressure mat, check that its outline will not be visible when it is under the carpet. Most types of carpet are thick enough to obscure the mat, but some kinds of cord carpet are too flexible and the shape shows through. Possibly a rug could be placed over the carpet at this point.

If you have a large dog that is sometimes left alone in the house, ensure that your pet is not able to trigger the alarm accidentally.

How it works
The circuit is the same as that of Project 1 (see Fig 2.1), except that SW2 (the mat) is wired differently (Fig 2.11). Pin 2 of IC1 is normally held high by R1. When someone steps on the mat, pin 2 is made low and the flip-flop is triggered. The alarm sounds until the reset button SW3 is pressed.

Construction
The layout of the circuit board is the same as that of Project 1 (Fig 2.4), except that R1 connects holes B4 and D4, and the mat is connected to the pins at D2 and J2. Assembling, testing and housing the project are the same as for Project 1. With this project

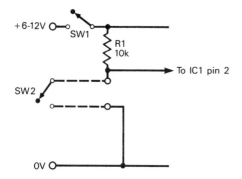

Figure 2.11 Project 3: pressure mat alarm circuit

the wires from the mat can run a long way under the carpet to another room where the circuit-box is located. For maximum security, the box is hidden from sight.

This project can be extended to include several mats, all wired in parallel, so that the alarm is triggered when any one mat is stepped on.

Components required
As for Project 1, substituting one or more pressure mats for the reed switch and magnet.

Project 4 Panic button

A panic button placed just inside the back door or front door of the home allows anyone answering the door to raise the alarm should an unwanted caller threaten to gain entry. A panic button can be located at other strategic situations, such as at the top of the stairs. Another use for such a button is beside the bed of an invalid or elderly person.

How it works
Push buttons sold for use as panic buttons usually have the button in red or are otherwise conspicuously marked. Often the surface of the button is recessed to make it less likely that the button will be pressed accidentally. Most such buttons have normally-open contacts and may be used in a circuit of the same kind as Project 3, with SW2 as the panic button. If preferred, an ordinary push-button with normally open contacts may be used instead. Several

19

buttons may be wired in parallel. Panic buttons can also be wired in parallel with one or more pressure mats. The alarm device that is fitted depends on the application. For household security, a solid-state buzzer or siren is suitable but, for use with an invalid or elderly person, there are a number of low-volume solid-state buzzers available. An LED or low-voltage (e.g. 6V, 0.1A, or 12V, 2.2A) lamp may be wired instead of or in parallel with the AWD. Also available are xenon flashing beacons which require only 40mA and operate on 12V. These too can be wired in parallel with or instead of the AWD.

Components required
As for Project 1, with a normally-open push-button for SW2, and suitable warning device(s)

Project 5 Bogus beam device

This is an intruder deterrent which pretends to be a security device but is nothing more than a circuit which flashes an LED. It relies on tricking a would-be intruder into believing that it could be dangerous to attempt to break in to your home. The flasher circuit is disguised as a beam projector, a control panel or some other component of a security system, and is located where it can be clearly (though not too obviously) seen from outside the house.

How it works
The circuit employs a special flasher ic (Fig 2.12) connected so as to flash an LED about once a second. This ic operates on only 1.5V and takes so little current that a single AA cell lasts for months,

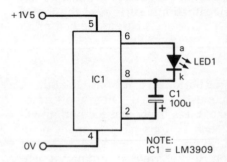

Figure 2.12 Project 5: bogus beam device circuit

running day and night. Current consumption is so small that it is not worth while to fit an on-off switch. The operation of the circuit is such that the flash is very short and of high intensity.

Construction

The circuit is quickly assembled on a scrap of strip-board (Fig 2.13). The body of the LED projects through a hole bored in the side of the case. If necessary, the LED can be connected by wires soldered to terminal pins at C8 and E8. The 1.5V cell, type AA or AAA, is contained in a single-cell battery box, or you can improvise contacts by using two solder-tags. A thick rubber band holds these firmly against the ends of the cell. The success of this project depends on housing the circuit in a convincing exterior. Its plastic box is dressed up by mounting a switch or two or a control knob on it. Add a tube (we used the body of an old coaxial plug) on one

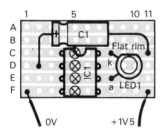

Figure 2.13 Project 5: stripboard layout

side to make it look as if it projects (or receives) a beam of invisible infra-red light. This imaginary beam is 'directed' across a doorway. A tilting mounting bracket could be used to give further realism.

Components required

Capacitor
C1   100μ electrolytic

Semiconductor
D1   light-emitting diode

Integrated circuit
IC1   LM3909 LED flasher

Miscellaneous
stripboard — any small scrap
1mm terminal pins (2 off)
suitable plastic enclosure and items to disguise it
8-way d.i.l. socket

Project 6 A booby trap

The element of surprise is a potent weapon against the intruder. A simple booby trap may be just as effective in scaring off the interloper as any of the more complex security systems. It is all a matter of ingenuity in baiting the trap. This project illustrates just one example of a booby trap. We leave it to the reader's inventiveness to devise even more original and effective ruses, based on the same principle.

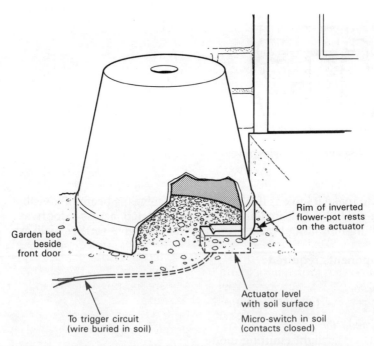

Rim of inverted
flower-pot rests
on the actuator

Garden bed
beside
front door

Actuator level
with soil surface

To trigger circuit
(wire buried in soil)

Micro-switch in soil
(contacts closed)

Figure 2.14 Project 6: a booby-trap. Instead of finding the front door key under the flower pot, the intruder sets off the alarm when lifting the pot. (Pot cut away in drawing to show the microswitch).

How it works

The basis of the trap (Fig 2.14) is a microswitch, with its contacts held closed by the weight of the flower-pot. As soon as anyone lifts the flower-pot, looking for the door-key so customarily hidden beneath it, the switch contacts open and the alarm sounds. The circuit for this project is the same as for Project 1, with the micro-switch taking the place of the reed switch SW2. Refer to Project 1 for constructional details. In certain applications, a mercury tilt-switch is an alternative to the microswitch.

Protecting a single article

A single valuable article, such as a video recorder, a painting or a silver trophy may be protected by a microswitch. The hidden switch is arranged so that its contacts are closed as long as the article is in place. When anyone attempts to 'lift' the article, the alarm sounds.

Components required

As for Project 1, substituting a microswitch for the reed switch and magnet.

Project 7 Fire detector alarm (excessive temperature)

One way of detecting fire is by sensing an excessively high temperature. This is relatively easy to do, making this project an simple one to build. Provided that the temperature sensor is placed where it is likely to be near to the source of fire, this method is a very reliable one. The device is cheap enough to make it feasible to have a number of detectors placed at different positions around the house.

Rooms with open fireplaces, the room in which the central heating boiler is located and any place where inflammable liquids are stored are obvious fire risks and a detector can be located in each such area. Since hot air and flames travel upward, the sensor should be placed high in the room. If you are limiting your system to one sensor, a suitable place is at the head of the stairs.

One point to consider is the temperature which is to be regarded as being excessive. If the device is set too low, it will be triggered on an exceptionally warm summer's day. On the other hand, if the device is set too high, it may not respond quickly enough unless the fire happens to break out very close by. A temperature of 50°C is usually taken as a satisfactory compromise. This is the temperature at which this project is designed to operate.

The project has its own audible warning device but several detectors can be connected to a single siren, through the household security system described in Chapters 5 to 7. The necessary modification of the project is described on p. 95.

Other methods of fire detection are the subjects of Projects 15 and 16.

How it works

The sensor is a *negative temperature coefficient* (ntc) thermistor. As the temperature of the thermistor is increased, its resistance decreases. The resistance of the thermistor specified for this project is 47k at 25°C. It falls to about 16k at 50°C.

In the circuit (Fig 2.15) the thermistor R1 and the variable resistor RV1 form a potential divider. As temperature increases, the voltage at the (−) input of the operational amplifier falls. The other potential divider in the circuit is formed by R2 and R3. With a 12V supply, the voltage at the (+) input of the amplifier is nominally 8V. However, it is pulled down below this level because the output of the amplifier is close to 0V and current flows from the potential divider, along R4. As a result of this, the voltage at the (+) input is about 7V. Since RV1 is set so as to give about 11V at the (-) input,

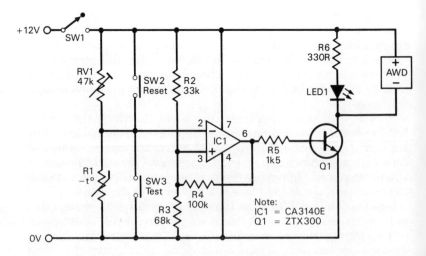

Figure 2.15 Project 7: fire alarm (excessive temperature)

24

this ensures that the amplifier output is low and the circuit is stable in this state. Q1 is off; the LED is not lit; the AWD is silent.

If the temperature of the thermistor is gradually increased, there is a gradual drop in voltage at the (−) input. When the voltage falls below 7V, the level at the (+) input, the output of the amplifier begins to rise. This causes current to flow through R4 *into* the R2/R3 potential divider, raising the voltage at the (+) input. This effect increases the difference between voltage levels, making the (-) input even more negative of the (+) input. This causes output to rise still further. This process continues until the output has risen almost to 12V. All of this takes place very quickly, producing a 'snap' action. Not only is the action rapid but it is not readily reversed. The voltage at the (+) input is now several volts higher than it was to start with.

If the thermistor were to cool slightly, and so raise the voltage at (−), this is not now enough to exceed the (+) input, so the amplifier remains with its output high. It is stable in this state. Q1 is turned on; the LED lights; the AWD sounds.

Once the circuit has been triggered by excessive temperature, the alarm continues to sound until the temperature falls very considerably. The reset button is provided to supply a high voltage to the (-) input to reset the circuit once the thermistor has cooled slightly below 50°C. The test button allows the user to check that the battery level is adequate and that the siren is operative.

The project operates on 6V to 12V. For 9V operation, use a 56k resistor for R3; for 6V operation, use 47k.

Construction

The layout diagram (Fig 2.16) shows the thermistor and AWD mounted on the circuit board. If preferred, one or both of these may be mounted externally. For example, the thermistor could be fixed in position above the central heating boiler, while the main circuit box with enclosed AWD is located in the living room.

Assemble the entire circuit, except that there is no need to connect the AWD until testing is complete. Adjust RV1 until the LED goes out. The voltage at IC1 pin 3 is about 7V with a 12V supply, 5V with a 9V supply, and 3V with a 6V supply. Adjust RV1 until the voltage at IC1 pin 2 is 1V below the supply voltage. Monitor the voltage at pin 2 as the thermistor is heated. With care, you can heat this by touching one of its leads gently with a hot soldering iron. The voltage falls and the LED comes on when it reaches the level at pin 3. Remove the heat source and after a second or two, press SW2; the LED goes out. Press SW3; the LED

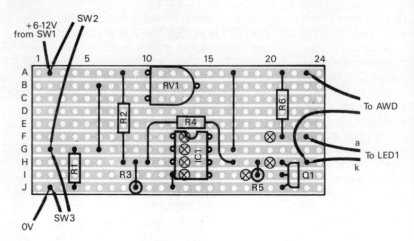

Figure 2.16 Project 7: stripboard layout

comes on. The AWD may now be connected and the whole assembly is ready to be placed inside its enclosure. If the thermistor is mounted on the board, perforate the enclosure in the region of the thermistor to allow hot air to circulate through it.

The project requires only 2mA so may be powered from a small battery, such as a 9V PP3 alkaline battery.

Calibration

Dip the sensor into a beaker of warm water at 50°C, and leave it for a minute to acquire the same temperature as the water. Start with the LED off and turn RV1 until the LED *just* comes on. Remove the sensor from the water. Press SW2. Check that the LED comes on again almost immediately the sensor is re-immersed in the hot water.

Components required

Resistors (see p.139)

R1	bead thermistor, 47k at 25°C
R2	33k
R3	68k (but see text)
R4	100k
R5	1k5
R6	330Ω
RV1	47k horizontal preset potentiometer

Semiconductors
LED1   light-emitting diode
Q1   ZTX300 npn transistor

Integrated circuit
CA3140   CMOS operational amplifier

Miscellaneous
SW1   single-pole single-throw toggle switch
SW2, SW3   push-to-make push-buttons (2 off)
solid-state audible warning device or solid-state siren
stripboard 63mm x 25mm
1mm terminal pins (6 off)
suitable plastic enclosure
8-way d.i.l. socket
battery holder
battery connector (PP3)

Project 8 Flood and overflow alarm

One of the worst domestic disasters is an overflowing tank in the loft which damages furniture, carpets and decorations. Even a washing machine emptying on to the kitchen floor instead of down the waste-pipe can cause a flood which quickly spreads to adjacent rooms. It is little use to wait until the water begins to drip through the ceiling or spread from under the kitchen door. By then, a major proportion of the damage will have been done and the flood may continue to spread after the water supply is turned off. This device supplies early warning of trouble. If the probe is suitably positioned, it can trigger the alarm to sound in time to avert much of the damage.

How it works
The circuit (Fig 2.17) is a version of the circuit of Project 1 (see Fig 2.1). The probe depends upon the electrical conductivity of water. Two electrodes are arranged so that flooding water forms a conductive bridge between them. Normally the input to pin 2 of IC1 is held at logic high because of R1. When water bridges the gap, current flows from R1 to the 0V rail. The logic level at pin 1 becomes low, setting the flip-flop, and the alarm sounds. The alarm continues to sound until the water has been removed from the probe and the reset button SW3 is pressed.

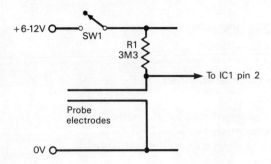

Figure 2.17 Project 8: flood/overflow alarm circuit

Construction

There are many ways of making the probe. Fig 2.18 shows a probe suitable for detecting when the water in a tank rises above a given level. A jack plug makes another level sensor. Connections are made to the tip and to the shaft. The plug is mounted vertically so that, as the water level rises, first the tip and eventually the shaft are immersed and contact is made between them. Mains plugs with two prongs are also useful as probes.

Another type of probe is indicated in Fig 2.19. This is made from a scrap of strip-board with alternate strips wired together. This can be used for sensing water level, but is particularly suitable for

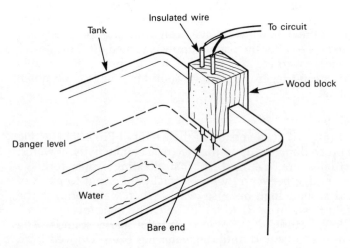

Figure 2.18 Probe used as tank water level detector

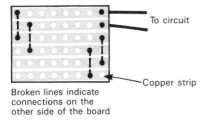

Broken lines indicate
connections on the
other side of the board

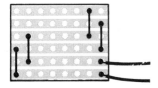

Figure 2.19 Probe made from stripboard. Dashed lines indicate connection to be made between strips.

detecting spraying water or isolated water drops. It could be used in the loft, for example, to detect water spraying from a fractured pipe. Several such probes, wired in parallel, are placed in various parts of the loft. A probe of this type is also useful for detecting a rain-shower and warning that the washing or the baby on the lawn should be taken in.

For details of construction of the circuit, see Project 1. R1 is connected between B4 and D4 (Fig 2.4) and the probe is wired to the terminal pins at D2 and J2. The probe or probes are sited externally on a long lead. The circuit enclosure is located in the living area, and it would usually be best to have a low-volume but distinctive solid-state buzzer as the audible warning device. The musical buzzer of Project 10 could be used here.

Components required
As for Project 1, but with a 3M3 resistor for R1 and the probe instead of SW2

3 Advanced circuits for intruder detection

Project 9 The Sentinel

This device is designed as a watchful eye with many applications. Its most obvious function is for intruder detection, but there are many other ways in which it can be usefully employed in the home or elsewhere. Use it to guard the door to warn you when junior wanders off-limits. Use it at night to watch for headlights when you are expecting callers. The Sentinel detects any small changes in the visual environment and tells you about it.

Several versions are possible. You can build a portable version, that can be set up wherever it is wanted for whatever job is on hand at the moment. Or you can make it a permanently installed part of your home security system. This project is a portable battery-powered version, which activates a low-level audible warning device. This can also be powered from a 6V, 9V or 12V DC mains adaptor. It requires only 10mA when quiescent and less than 50mA when activated. If you need a louder alarm, substitute a solid-state siren for the low-level AWD. Alternatively, you could substitute a miniature relay for the AWD and connect it to the household security system described in Chapters 5 to 7.

How it works

Light from the area being watched passes through a hole in the case, and falls on the sensor. The sensor is a phototransistor (Q1, Fig 3.1). In the prototype we used a BPX25, but any general-purpose npn phototransistor will do.

Variation in the amount of light falling on the phototransistor causes a variation in the current flowing through R1, and thus produces a varying voltage at point A. The varying voltage is fed to an operational amplifier (IC1), wired as a subtractor. The output

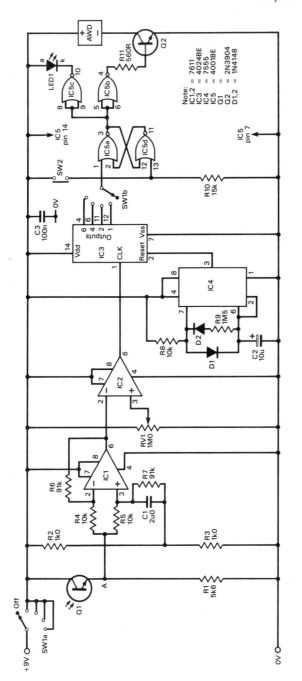

Figure 3.1 Project 9: circuit diagram of the sentinel

of the amplifier is proportional to the *difference* between its inputs. Since point A is connected to both inputs through 10k resistors, the difference between the inputs is zero and the output should also be zero. Whether the light level is high or low, the amplifier has zero output.

The key to the way the Sentinel works is the capacitor C1. If any *rapid* change occurs in the amount of light, as when a person passes across the field of view, for example, the voltage at the (−) input changes *instantly*. But C1 makes the change at the (+) input change *slowly*. For a fraction of a second the inputs receive *different voltages*, and the output rises or falls. Since R6 and R7 are about nine times greater than R4 and R5, there is nine-fold amplification of input voltage differences at this stage.

The circuit is thus designed to respond to rapid changes in light, such as would be caused by an intruder, a flashlamp, or the cat jumping out of the window, but not to slow changes resulting from clouds obscuring the Sun, or variations of light level with time of day.

The reference to 'zero output' above needs further clarification. Operational amplifiers operate on a dual supply so that, *with respect to the amplifier*, the power supply lines are not 0V and +9V (assuming the circuit is being run from a 9V supply), but −4.5V and +4.5V. Then we can speak of the amplifier's output as 0V. With respect to the voltages shown in Fig 3.1, the steady output of the amplifier is about +4.5V, that is to say, it lies midway between the voltage of the two power lines. Similar reasoning also applies if the power supply is 6V or 12V.

IC2 is wired as a comparator to give an all-or-nothing response to changes in the output of IC1. To achieve this, RV1 is set to give a standard voltage at its wiper a little below +4.5V (again assuming a 9V supply). Since IC2 has no feedback resistor, its gain is exceedingly large and the output of IC2 swings right up to +9V. This is the equivalent of a logical high. Whenever the output of IC1 swings above +4.5V, the output of IC2 swings sharply to 0V, the equivalent of logical low. This means that whenever there is *rapid* change in the light falling on Q1, the output of IC2 changes from logic high to logic low, possibly several times. IC3 is a 7-stage counter which registers a count every time its clock input falls from high to low. It counts the swings.

RV1 acts as a sensitivity control, since it sets the voltage level at which the output of IC2 is affected by changes in the output of IC1. The other control can be referred to as a *vigilance control*. A sentinel does not necessarily raise the alarm at the first hint of danger. A sentinel is alerted but, if nothing further happens during the next few seconds, decides that nothing is amiss. On the other hand, repeated disturbances indicate that danger threatens and the alarm is given.

The switch SW1b selects one of four outputs from the counter. This determines how many disturbances (logic highs and lows) are needed to trigger the alarm. If output 1 is selected, the alarm is triggered at the first disturbance. The other outputs trigger the alarm at the 2nd, 8th and 32nd disturbances respectively. This allows you to decide how vigilant the Sentinel is to be. If you want to avoid a false alarm when the light from headlamps of a passing car flashes through the window, set vigilance to output 4. Unless you live in a particularly busy street, passing cars are unlikely to produce as many as 8 disturbances in a short time. But an intruder directing a flashlamp around the room is likely to produce more flashes — and trigger the alarm.

The counter is reset every 10 seconds by a high pulse from the clock (IC4). If the number of disturbances occurring in 10 seconds is fewer than that selected by SW1b, they are 'forgotten'. In this way, we considerably reduce the possibility of false alarms under 'noisy' conditions.

The timer ic is operating with a short 'high' output and relatively long 'low' output, the inverse of its usual duty cycle. This action is the result of the two diodes, D1 and D2. The capacitor charges rapidly through R8 and D1, giving a short 'high' output period. It discharges very slowly through R9 and D2, giving a long 'low' output period.

When you set up the Sentinel, press SW2 to reset the flip-flop (the cross-connected NOR gates of IC5). Hold down SW2 for 10 seconds until the counter has been reset too. While you are waiting, the AWD sounds. If your version of the Sentinel is wired to the home security system or to a loud siren, inactivate the system at this stage. As soon as the counter is cleared, the flip-flop can reset and its output (pin 3) goes low. The AWD stops sounding. At the same time the output at pin 10 goes low, turning on the LED to indicate that the Sentinel is activated. Disturbances are then counted until enough occur in a 10-second period to make the selected counter output go high. This sets the flip-flop. The output at pin 10 goes high, turning off the LED. The output at pin 4 goes high, turning on Q2 and the audible warning device.

Since the action of the circuit depends on rapid changes of light intensity, the Sentinel works best under contrasty lighting conditions. Outdoors, it is most sensitive in open sunlit areas. A white wall in the background is ideal, as shadows cast on the wall by an intruder will soon be spotted by the Sentinel's eye. Indoors, it works best if its field of view includes a well-lit light-coloured wall, or it can see the sky through a window. In more specialised applications, place it so that change of light level is maximal. For example, to guard a valuable piece of equipment, such as a video recorder, hide the Sentinel behind the video so that the hole is completely blocked by it. When the video is removed, the sudden flood of light into the phototransistor triggers the alarm.

Construction
The layout diagrams (Fig 3.2) show the circuit assembled on two pieces of stripboard cut to fit into slots formed in the sides of the case. Alternatively, build the circuit on a single board of larger size. It is simplest to begin with Board 1, with the circuit stage shown on the left-hand side of Fig 3.1 and work toward the right. When Board 1 is complete, move on to Board 2.

As you proceed from stage to stage, check voltages with respect to the 0V rail. Voltages are given below assuming a 9V supply. Voltages are proportionate with a 6V or 12V supply. The diagram shows the connections for the ICL7611 operational amplifier. You can substitute CA3140, in which case omit the connection to pin 8.

The voltage at point A is approximately 1V in a well-lit room, falling if you shade the phototransistor with your hand, and rising almost to 9V in bright sunlight. The voltage at the junction of R2 and R3 is a steady 4.5V. The output of IC1 is about 4.5V, rising or falling by a fraction of a volt if the phototransistor is rapidly shaded or uncovered, but staying close to 4.5V if changes in light intensity are *very* slow.

Adjust RV1 so that the output of IC2 is 9V. Then turn RV1 until it *just* begins to fall. Now, shading the phototransistor makes the output of IC2 fall sharply to 0V, returning to 9V almost immediately. The clock output (IC4) is low, with a very short high (9V) pulse every 10 seconds. The needle of a voltmeter stays at 0V with a short upward 'kick' every 10 seconds. The counter outputs all go low every 10 seconds, then show an increasing binary count if you wave your hand in front of the phototransistor. Output at pin 3 of IC5 goes high and the LED comes on when SW2 is pressed, and the counter has reset. Output at pin 11 is the inverse of this. When the selected count is reached, output at pin 3 goes low, and the AWD sounds.

The circuit is mounted in a case, with the phototransistor in line with a hole in the side of the case. This limits the field of view,

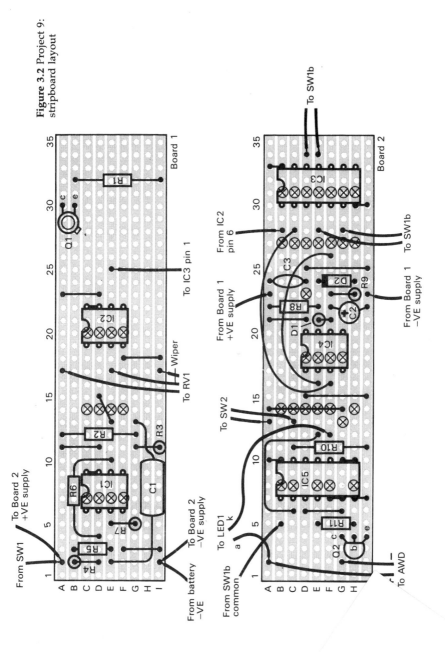

Figure 3.2 Project 9: stripboard layout

allowing the Sentinel to concentrate on events in a restricted area. It is possible to mount a lens at the hole, so as to focus an image of a more distant scene, and thus allow the device to observe an even more restricted field at a distance.

The mounting of the other components is a matter of placing them so that the shadow of your hand does not trigger the circuit while you are making adjustments. The AWD must be bolted to the case to increase its loudness. Alternatively, the leads from the circuit-board are taken to a 2-pin socket. From there a long lead runs to the AWD or to a solid-stage siren.

Components required

Resistors (see p. 139)

R1	5k6
R2, R3	1k
R4, R5	10k
R6, R7	91k
R8	10k
R9	1M5
R10	15k
R11	560Ω

Capacitors

C1	2μF polyester
C2	10μF electrolytic
C3	100nF polyester or ceramic disc

Semiconductors

D1, D2	1N4148 npn signal diode
LED1	light-emitting diode
Q1	phototransistor
Q2	2N3904 npn transistor

Integrated circuits

IC1, IC2	ICL7611 CMOS operational amplifier (or CA3140)
IC3	4024BE CMOS 7-stage binary ripple counter
IC4	7555 (or MC1455) CMOS timer
IC5	4001BE CMOS quadruple 2-input NOR gate

Miscellaneous

SW1	2-pole, 6-way rotary switch
SW2	press-to-make push-button

stripboard, 2 pieces 35 holes by 9 strips, or to fit slots in box
terminal pins (19 off)
suitable plastic enclosure

8-pin ic sockets (3 off)
14-pin ic sockets (2 off)
knob for S1 battery connector (PP3)
lens and lens mounting (optional)

Project 10 Programmable alert

Although a strident note or a wailing siren is usually the preferred
form of audible warning device for the projects in this book, there
are certain applications for which this is not appropriate. In
situations in which raising the alarm is not a matter of life and
death, and in which it is more important that the neighbours
should not be disturbed, a rather quieter and more melodious
sound is demanded. This programmable alert plays a sequence of
4 notes when switched on. You select which notes it is to play, so
it is possible to have more than one such alert in the home, each
with a different sequence, to alert you to various minor hazards.

How it works
The system diagram (Fig 3.3) shows that the first stage is a clock,
or astable multivibrator, running at approximately 1Hz. This
produces a square wave that is fed to an 8-stage counter. The
counter ic incorporates a decoder so that, at each count, one and
only one of its eight output terminals is at logic high (+6V), the
remainder being at logic low (0V). As each pulse arrives from the
clock, the outputs 0 to 7 go high in turn. Outputs 0 to 3 each
correspond to one note of the tune.

Although each output goes to the supply voltage when it is high,
the amount of current that flows from any given output depends
on the value of the resistance connected to it. The outputs
are *weighted*. Thus each output produces a different current. It is
the amount of current that eventually determines the pitch of each
note.

The next stage is an operational amplifier wired as a summer (or
adder). As each counter output goes high in turn, different
currents flow to the summer and, as a result, the output of the
summer varies in voltage. Its voltage steps from one level to
another, corresponding to the notes of the tune. However, the
voltage produced is negative. This is why we need a second
amplifer to invert the voltage steps, making them positive. This
varying voltage (one step per note) is fed to a voltage controlled
oscillator (VCO). The output of this is a square wave signal of

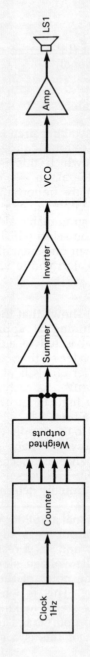

Figure 3.3 Project 10: system diagram of the programmable alert

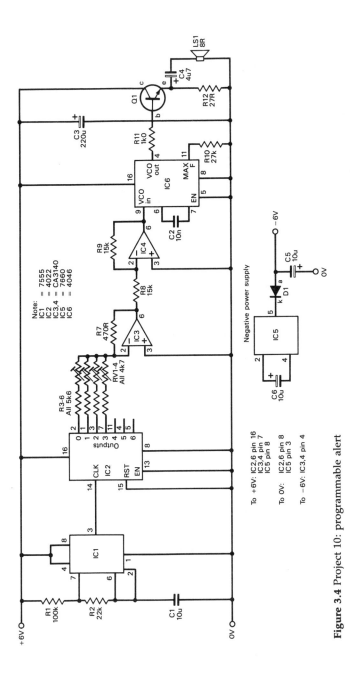

Figure 3.4 Project 10: programmable alert

varying audio frequency. A single transistor amplifier provides the extra power needed to drive the loudspeaker.

The circuit diagram (Fig 3.4) shows that the clock (IC1) is built from a 7555 timer. Its output (pin 3) goes directly to the counter (IC2). Weighting of its outputs is achieved by a fixed resistor and variable potentiometer at outputs 0 to 3. The required resistance ranges from about 6k to 10k, depending on what pitch each note is to have.

IC3 is wired as a conventional op amp summer. The reason for using a summer, even though only one counter output is active at a time, is that the (−) input of the op amp is a *virtual earth*. What happens when a current flows from one of the counter outputs is that the amplifier output swings negative, drawing *the whole current* on through R7 and *into* the output of the amplifier. The negative swing of the output is just enough to take in all the current, leaving pin 2 always at 0V. None of the current flowing from an output of IC2 can wander along through other resistors to the other outputs. This means that each note of the tune can be set independently of the others. Because the weighting resistors are about 8k (total for each output) and R7 is 4k7 and, because the op amp is wired as an inverting amplifier, the gain of the summer is about −(4.7/8), or roughly −0.6. For an input voltage of +6V (logic high), its output voltage varies around −3.6V. The next stage turns this upside down. IC4 is an op amp wired as an inverter with gain of −1, so its output swings positive.

IC5 is a complete phase-locked loop (PLL) ic. The nature of a PLL ic need not concern us here, except to say that a VCO is an essential part of a PLL and we are using just the VCO here. The maximum frequency of the oscillator is fixed by the capacitor C2 and the resistor R10. If the input voltage is 0V the frequency is zero — silence. As voltage increases, so does the pitch. The output of this ic is a square wave from pin 4. This signal is fed to Q1 to drive the loudspeaker. C3 is a decoupling capacitor to isolate the rest of the circuit from the effects of the switching of the relatively large current through Q1 and R12.

The circuit takes just over 50mA, so it is powered by four AA or AAA cells in a battery holder. The operational amplifiers need a −6V supply. This is provided by IC5, a voltage converter. Note the polarity of C5.

Construction
The circuit is built on two pieces of stripboard, cut so as to fit into slots in the walls of the plastic case. Fig 3.5 shows the stripboard

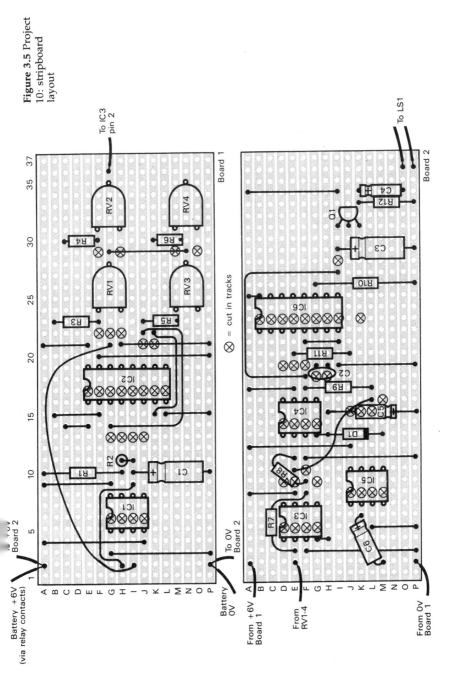

Figure 3.5 Project 10: stripboard layout

layout. Begin with the astable multivibrator IC1 and check that it runs at about 1Hz. Then wire up IC2. Use a voltmeter to monitor the outputs from IC2; each goes high for about 1 second every 8 seconds. Now solder in R3-R6 and RV1-RV4.

Before installing the op amps, you need the negative power supply (IC5). Connect this up and check that its output is −6V. It may fall to −5.5V when the circuit is in operation, but this is nothing to worry about. Now wire up IC3. As the circuit runs, monitor its output. It is about 0V (with respect to the 0V rail) when outputs 4 to 7 are high, but swings between about −3V and −5V when outputs 0 to 3 are high.

Now add IC4 and monitor its output, which swings between about +3V and +5V when outputs 0 to 3 are high. Connect IC6, Q1 and associated components. When power is applied a 4-note 'tune' is heard repeatedly, with 4-second gaps between each repetition. Adjust RV1 to RV4 until you obtain the tune you require. If the pitch is overall too high, increase the value of R10.

To operate the circuit from one of the detection devices, replace the detector's built-in AWD with a relay which has a coil rated to operate on 6V, 9V or 12V, depending on the supply voltage of the device. A low-power miniature or ultra-miniature relay intended for circuit-board mounting is suitable as its contacts have to switch only 50mA. The contacts of the relay are wired between the positive battery terminal and pin at A2 on Board 1 (Fig 3.6).

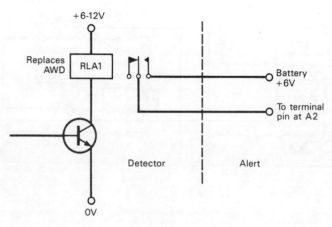

Figure 3.6 Operating the alert from one of the detector circuits

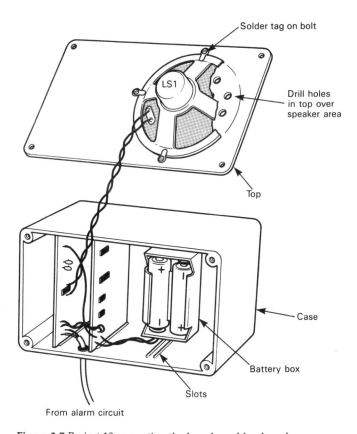

Figure 3.7 Project 10: mounting the boards and loudspeaker

Fig 3.7 shows how the circuit boards and loudspeaker are mounted in the plastic box. If you prefer, the circuit board of the detection device can be mounted in the same box.

Drill an array of holes in the top where the loudspeaker is to be mounted. Also drill three holes just outside where the rim of the loudspeaker will be. Each hole takes a small bolt, threaded with a solder tag, a shake-proof washer and a nut. As the bolt is tightened, position the tag to that its shank grips the rim of the loudspeaker. The battery box is held in place by double-sided self-adhesive pads.

Components required
Resistors (see p. 139)
R1	100k
R2	22k
R3-R6	5k6 (4 off)
R7	470Ω
R8, R9	15k (2 off)
R10	27k
R11	1k
R12	27
RV1-RV4	4k7 miniature horizontal preset resistors

Capacitors
C1	10µ electrolytic
C2	10n polyester
C3	220µ electrolytic
C4	4µ7 electrolytic

Semiconductors
D1	1N4148 silicon signal diode
Q1	npn junction transistor

Integrated circuits
IC1	7555 CMOS timer
IC2	4022BE CMOS divide-by-8 counter with 1-of-8 outputs
IC3,IC4	CA3140 CMOS operational amplifier (2 off)
IC5	7660 voltage converter
IC6	4046BE CMOS phase-locked loop

Miscellaneous
LS1   loudspeaker, 8Ω
stripboard 2 pieces, 37 holes by 16 strips
1mm terminal pins (8 off)
suitable plastic enclosure
8-way d.i.l. sockets (4 off)
16-way d.i.l. sockets (2 off)
nut, solder tag, bolt (3 off)
4-cell AA or AAA battery holder
battery clip (PP3)

Project 11 Ultrasonic intruder detector

This is a sensitive stand-alone device for detecting the presence of an intruder in a room. It depends upon the Doppler effect. You observe this effect when, for example, a fire-engine rushes past you. As the engine passes, the pitch of its siren appears to drop suddenly. What is happening is that the pitch is apparently raised when the engine is approaching and apparently lowered when it is receding. At the moment the engine passes you, there is an apparent fall in pitch.

The same principle applies to sound that is being reflected from a moving object. If a room contains a source of sound, the sound being reflected from a person moving towards the listener has an apparently higher pitch. the sound being reflected from a receding person has an apparently lower pitch.

With sounds of audible frequencies, the effect of a person moving around the room is insufficient to produce a noticeable change of pitch — unless the person is moving at speeds of 100km/h or more, like a fire-engine answering an urgent call! However, this device makes use of sound of very high frequency, higher than that detectable by the human ear. We call it *ultrasound*. This has the advantage that the person is unaware that the device is operating in the room. It also means that the normal motion of the person creates a perceptible Doppler effect. The circuit is designed to emit ultrasound and to detect variations in the apparent pitch of this sound when reflected from a moving person.

How it works

The circuit consists of two parts, the transmitter and the receiver, though both are built on the same piece of stripboard. The transmitter is driven by an astable multivibrator operating at 80kHz (IC1 Fig 3.8). The waveform of its output is asymmetrical; it is high for longer than it is low. This signal is fed to a D-type flip-flop (IC2), wired so that it gives a symmetrical output at 40kHz. The signal from output Q and its inverse from output $\bar{Q}$ are sent to opposite sides of a crystal (XTAL1) specially cut to oscillate at 40kHz. Ultrasound radiates from this to all parts of the room.

The ultrasound reflected from objects in the room is received by XTAL2, a similar crystal cut to resonate at the same frequency. The arriving ultrasound makes the crystal vibrate and this causes an alternating potential difference to appear across the crystal. This p.d. is amplified by the high gain amplifier consisting of Q1 and Q2. This is rectified by D1 and D2, and the high-frequency component of the sound is filtered away to the 0V rail through the filter consisting of C5 and R7. This leaves a steady voltage at C7.

The ultra-sound received by XTAL2 consists of a mixture of the

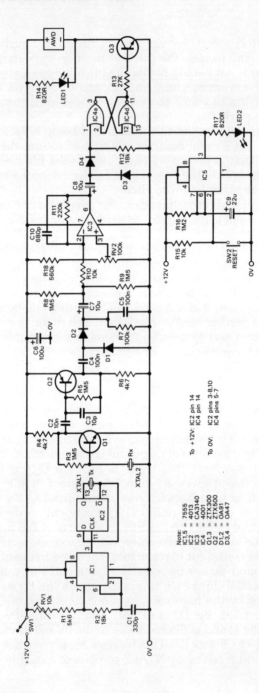

Figure 3.8 Project 11: ultrasonic intruder detector

original ultrasound (40kHz) reflected from stationary objects and ultra-sound of slightly higher and lower frequencies reflected from moving persons or objects. When two slightly different frequencies are mixed the phenomenon of *beats* occurs. You may have noticed this effect when two similar motors are running, but not at quite the same speed. This can happen in twin-engine aeroplanes if their engines are not perfectly synchronised. In addition to the sound of the engines we hear a throbbing sound. The sound throbs (i.e. increases and decreases in volume) at a rate equal to the *difference* in the frequencies of the two component sounds.

If, for example, ultra-sound of frequency of 40000Hz is reflected from a moving object and then has a frequency of 40002Hz, their combined sound throbs or 'beats' at 2Hz. If movement is even slower, the reflected ultrasound may have a frequency of, say, 40000.5Hz or 39999.7Hz, in which case beats of 0.5Hz and 0.3Hz are produced.

We have said that the voltage at C7 is steady but, if there is movement in the room and beats are produced, the *fluctuations* in the amplitude are *not* filtered out by C5 and R7. The voltage at C7 *fluctuates* at the beat frequency of a few hertz or less. The small fluctuations at C7 are amplified by the next stage IC3 and then rectified again. With no beats, the voltage at pin 1 is zero, or logical low.

As beats occur, the voltage at pin 1 swings to logical high. This triggers the flip-flop. Its output at pin 11 changes from low to high, Q3 is turned on, LED1 comes on, and the AWD sounds. The flip-flop remains in the set state and the alarm continues to sound until the source of beats is removed and the circuit is reset.

In most circuits we reset a flip-flop by a simple push-button, but something more elaborate is required here. The flip-flop is reset by a long low pulse generated by the monostable IC5. The output of IC5 is normally low, but goes high for about 30s when SW2 is pressed. This resets the flip-flop. The long resetting pulse gives the operator the opportunity to leave the room after resetting the circuit. The circuit is so sensitive to motion that, without the delay, it would be virtually impossible to leave without triggering the alarm.

This extreme sensitivity is invaluable for detecting intruders but can lead to problems with false alarms. If the window is a left open, a curtain flapping in the draught may easily trigger the device. Currents of air, such as might be caused by strong sunshine coming through the window and heating an object in the room may also trigger it. In testing the prototype, we found that an electric convector heater in the same room frequently triggered the circuit, even with the sensitivity set low. It has been known for insects such as flies to be detected! Therefore it is important to ensure absolute stillness in the room.

Construction

The circuit is built on a single board (Fig 3.9) with the transmitter and receiver crystals at opposite ends of the board, about 150mm apart. You will probably need to enlarge the holes slightly to accommodate the terminal pins of the ultrasonic crystals, and you may need to drill an additional hole if the pins are not spaced to match with the matrix of the board.

First assemble the transmitter circuit. An oscilloscope is needed to check the operation of the circuit stage by stage. If you do not possess such an instrument, take particular care with assembly and check the critical voltages mentioned below. The astable produces a square wave of 80kHz, which may be monitored with an oscilloscope at pin 3 of IC1. Adjust RV1 to obtain precisely 80kHz. In the absence of an oscilloscope, adjust this resistor later to obtain optimal performance. The output of IC2 (pin 12 and 13) is a square wave at 40kHz.

Next assemble the first stage of the receiver circuit. The voltage at the emitter of Q1 shows an approximate sine wave, frequency 40kHz, amplitude. Since this is a high-gain amplifier there is a tendency for it to oscillate at high frequency in the absence of ultrasound (e.g. with IC1 removed from its socket). Capacitor C3 is intended to prevent this; if any oscillation is present, try increasing the value of C3. Add the rectifying and filtering components i.e. as far as C7. The voltage at the cathode of D2 (measured by a voltmeter) is approximately 0.3V in the absence of ultrasound. With ultrasound, the voltage swings irregularly between about 3V and 4V. Waving your arm around in front of the receiver crystal results in a temporary upsurge in the voltage.

After you have built the next amplifier stage (IC3), set RV2 to give a voltage of 1V. The output (pin 6) is close to 0V in the absence of ultrasound. With ultrasound present, waving your arm around produces violent voltage swings ranging right up to 12V.

Add C8, D3, D4, R12 and IC4. The voltage at pin 1 is zero when there is ultrasound but no movement. With movement it frequently swings to 12V. Build the resetting circuit (IC5 etc). LED2 comes on for about 30s when SW2 is pressed. Check that pressing SW2 resets the flip-flop (pin 3 high, pin 11 low) and that motion sets it. Finally add R14, R15, Q3, LED1 and the AWD.

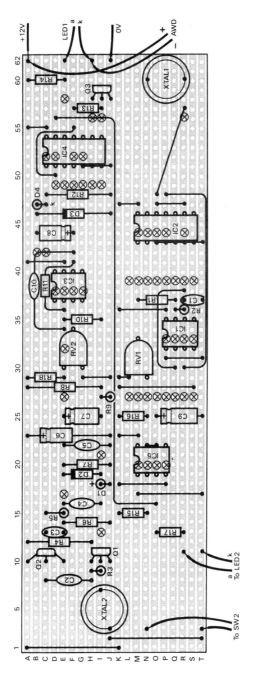

Figure 3.9 Project 11: stripboard layout

49

The circuit requires about 25mA, so battery operation from eight D cells is feasible, particularly if alkaline cells or re-chargeable cells are used. Alternatively, use a 12V dc mains adaptor. The enclosure is large enough to house the circuit board and battery holder (if used). It requires apertures for the transmitter and receiver crystals. The power switch SW1, reset button SW2 and the two LEDs are mounted on the lid of the case. Bore a small hole in the case so that a screwdriver can be inserted to adjust RV2. Adjusting RV2 is a way of setting the sensitivity of the device. The AWD can be mounted inside the case, or on extension leads. Instead of the AWD you can fit a relay for connecting the device into the household system (p. 95).

Components required
Resistors (see p.139)

R1	5k6
R2,R12	18k (2 off)
R3,R5,R8,R9	1M5 (4 off)
R4,R6	4k7 (2 off)
R7	100k
R10,R15	10k (2off)
R11	220k
R13	27k
R14,17	820Ω
R16	1M2
R18	560k

RV1 10k miniature horizontal preset
RV2 100k miniature horizontal preset

Capacitors

C1	330p polystyrene
C2	10n polyester
C3	10p metallised ceramic plate
C4,C5	100n polyester (2 off)
C6	100μ electrolytic
C7,C8	10μ electrolytic (2 off)
C9	22μ electrolytic
C10	680p polystyrene

Semiconductors

D1,D2	OA91 germanium point contact diode (2 off)
D3,D4	OA47 germanium gold-bonded diode (2 off)
LED1,LED2	light-emitting diode (2 off)

Q1,Q3	ZTX300 (2 off)
Q2	ZTX500

Integrated circuits

IC1,IC5	7555 CMOS timer (2 off)
IC2	4013BE CMOS dual D-type flip-flop
IC3	CA3140 CMOS operational amplifier
IC4	4001BE quadruple 2-input NOR gate

Miscellaneous

S1	single-pole single-throw toggle switch
S2	push-to-make push-button
XTAL1	40kHz ultra-sonic transmitter
XTAL2	40kHz ultra-sonic receiver

stripboard 62 holes by 20 strips
1mm terminal pins (8 off)
suitable plastic enclosure
8-way d.i.l. sockets (3 off)
14-way d.i.l. sockets (2 off)
solid-state audible warning device or solid-state siren
8-cell battery-holder and PP3 battery connector or 12Vdc mains
adaptor

Project 12 Automatic lamp and radio switch

This project makes use of relays to switch mains current. Those who have not had previous experience of constructing projects in which mains current is used are advised to seek the help and advice of an experienced person before building this project.

One of the well-established ways of deterring a potential burglar is to leave lights on in the house when it is unoccupied. Another ploy is to leave a radio playing. If you are going out just for an evening, it is a simple enough matter to switch on the lights and the radio before you leave. If you are going away for a week-end or for a longer period, this plan has drawbacks.

There are a number of devices on the market that switch lights on and off automatically. Some of these work by detecting when dusk falls and turning on a lamp for a few hours. Other devices consist of a time switch that can be programmed to turn the light on and off at pre-set times. The trouble with many of these is that they repeat a regular sequence night after night, giving away to the observant watcher the fact that control is automatic.

This project combines the best features of many of the commercial devices with a few novel features of its own. The device controls two lamps and a radio set (or TV) independently. It operates by detecting dusk so it switches on the lamps on a particularly dull day, too. The lamps and radio are switched as follows:

Lamp 1: Comes on at dusk, remains on for the whole evening, and is turned off either 2½ hours or 5 hours later.

Lamp 2: Operates for the same period as lamp 1, but is switched on and off apparently at random during that period.

Radio: During the period from dawn until lamp 1 finally goes off (i.e. daytime and evening) the radio is switched on and off apparently at random.

The provision of two lamps is an important safeguard against the failure of one of the lamps during a prolonged period of operation. When using single-lamp devices, we have on several occasions returned from a holiday only to find that the lamp has burned out. Intruder deterrence was inoperative for perhaps the whole of the period we were away.

Random switching

This depends upon the generation of a pseudo-random sequence of binary digits. The circuit that does this is based on a shift register, as shown in Fig 3.10. The shift register consists of a series of seven registers connected so that, at every clock pulse, the data held in each register is shifted to the next register in the series. The data in the 6th and 7th registers are fed to an exclusive-OR gate and the output from this gate is fed to the first register. The exclusive-OR gate is sometimes known as a 'same or different' gate. Its output is low when its two inputs are alike (both '0' or both '1') but is high when they differ (a '0' and a '1').

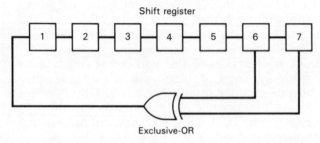

Shift register

Exclusive-OR

Figure 3.10 Circuit for generating pseudo-random sequences

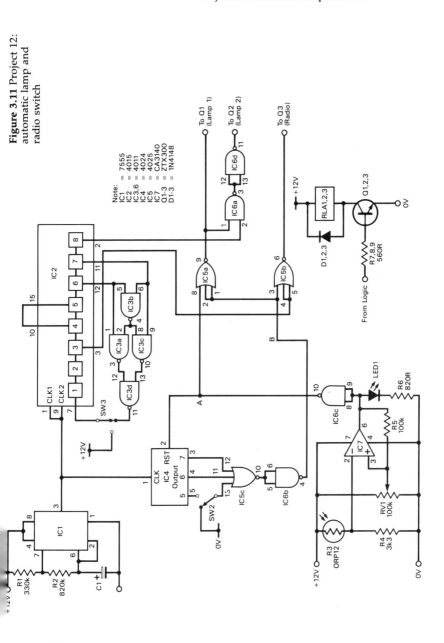

Figure 3.11 Project 12: automatic lamp and radio switch

The action of the generator can be simulated on paper by first writing down any seven binary digits:

1 1 0 0 1 0 0 (Ex-OR of 6th and 7th is 0)
Shift the data along and put '0' in register 1:
0 1 1 0 0 1 0 (Ex-OR of 6th and 7th is 1)
Shift the data along and put '1' in register 1:
1 0 1 1 0 0 1 (Ex-OR of 6th and 7th is 1)

If you continue this operation, you obtain an irregular and apparently random sequence of binary digits. It repeats after 127 shifts and, since shifts occur at 10-minute intervals in this project, the sequence runs for over 20 hours before repeating. It would require an extraordinarily patient observer to detect that this is not a random sequence.

How it works
Fig 3.11 shows the shift register (IC2) driven by a clock (IC1) running at approximately 0.0016Hz (1 cycle in 10 minutes). IC2 contains two 4-bit shift registers which are connected externally to make an 8-bit register. The four NAND gates of IC3 are wired together to act as an exclusive-OR gate. This accepts the data from the 6th and 7th registers and feeds the resultant exclusive-OR to the first register. SW3 is used to prevent an 'all-zero' situation. The exclusive-OR of two '0' inputs is '0' so, if all registers hold zero when the circuit is switched on, an endless succession of zeros circulates through the registers. SW3 is switched to the 12V supply when the circuit is first run, to put a few '1's into the registers; then it is switched to the exclusive-OR gate.

In the description which follows, we consider each 24-hour period to be divided into three parts: day, evening and night. The circuit distinguishes between these parts by means of the logic levels at two points A and B (Fig 3.11). Ambient light level is detected by the sub-circuit at the bottom left of Fig 3.11. The sensor is a light-dependent resistor, R3. The resistance of this increases when light levels are low.

As dusk approaches, the resistance of R3 increases, causing the voltage at the (−) input of the operational amplifier (IC7) to fall. The output of the amplifier rises from 0V to 12V (logic low to logic high). The action of the amplifier is the same as that of IC1 in Project 7 (Fig 2.15). As explained in that project, an amplifier connected in this way has a 'snap' action. It changes rapidly when the predetermined light level is reached. Also, once the change in output has occurred, it is not reversed by small reversals of light level. The increase in output from IC7 turns on the LED1. At the same time the output of the NAND gate (IC6, pin 10) goes low. Thus a high logic level at A indicates light conditions (= day); a low level indicates dark conditions (= evening or night).

During the day, the high level at A holds the reset of the counter (IC4) high, preventing the counter from operating. At dusk, A becomes low and the counter begins to count pulses from the clock, incrementing every 10 minutes. During the day and early evening the outputs from stages 5 to 7 of the counter are low, so the output of the NOR gate is high. Output 5 goes high and the NOR gate output goes low on the 16th count, i.e. 160 minutes after dusk. This indicates the end of the 'evening', and the beginning of 'night'

To obtain a longer 'evening', switch SW2 is set to 0V so that 'evening' does not end until stage 6 goes high, on the 32nd count, 320 minutes after dusk. From then on, until stage 7 has gone high then low, at least one of the inputs of the NOR gate is high and it is 'night'.

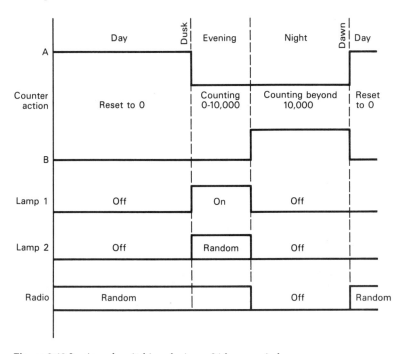

Figure 3.12 Logic and switching during a 24 hour period

Stage 7 does not go low again until the 128th count, 1280 minutes (21 hours) after dusk but, long before this, the Sun will have risen again and the counter will have been reset ready to resume counting at dusk on the following day. The output of the NOR gate is inverted by the NAND gate (IC 6 pin 4). Thus a low level at point B indicates 'day' or 'evening'; a high level indicates 'night'

Fig 3.12 shows the changes in logic levels at A and B during a period of just over 24 hours. The state of A and B is analysed by NOR and NAND gates to control the lamps and radio set. The gate outputs control transistor switches, which in turn operate relays.

Lamp 1: On when A and B are both low (evening)

Lamp 2: On when A and B are both low (evening) AND when the data in register 8 is high.

Radio: On when B is low (day and evening) and the data in register 3 is low.

The fact that lamp 2 and the radio use data from two different registers, make it appear that the radio and Lamp 2 are switched independently.

Construction

The circuit is best powered by a 12V dc mains adaptor. First build the clock (IC1 and associated components, Fig 3.13) but with a 470n

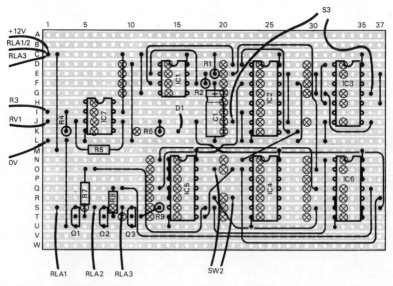

Figure 3.13 Project 12: stripboard layout of mains board

capacitor for C1. This makes the clock run 1000 times faster, speeding up the action of the circuit while it is being built and tested. Build the exclusive-OR network of gates (IC3) and check that it operates correctly (see above). Then add the shift register and connect the clock. Switching SW3 to +12V soon results in all registers holding '1'. Pin 11 of IC3 is low. When SW3 is switched to direct the exclusive-OR output into the shift register, pin 11 alternates irregularly between '0' and '1'.

Next build the light-sensing circuit. R3 may temporarily be connected by a short lead. The voltage at the junction of R3 and R4 falls as the light intensity decreases. With R3 exposed to ordinary room lighting, adjust RV1 until the output of IC7 *just* falls to 0V. Covering R3 with your hand makes the output swing sharply to 12V.

Connect IC4, IC5 and IC6. There is no need to fit SW2 yet; make a temporary wired connection between the terminal pins at O19 and R21. With R3 uncovered, pins 3, 4 and 5 of IC4 are low. Covering R3 allows the counter to operate; monitor stage 1 (pin 12) which is alternating between high and low at half the clock rate. After about 10 seconds, pin 5 goes high. The outputs of the logic gates are as follows:

IC5, pin 9: low when R3 exposed; high for about 10s after it has been covered

IC6, pin 11: low when R3 exposed; alternates irregularly between high and low for about 10s after it has been covered.

IC5, pin 6: alternates irregularly until about 10s after R3 has been covered; is then low until R3 is exposed.

Now wire up the transistor switches. The relays are mounted on separate boards, the exact layout depending upon the type of relays used. Fig 3.14 shows the layout for a pair of typical relays with mains contacts, and with pin spacing suitable for strip-board mounting. The leads carrying mains currents are cut from a length of light-duty mains flex.

Remove the copper strips completely in the region of the contact terminals pins. Leads are soldered direct to the terminal pins of the relays. Care must be taken with soldering to ensure that stray strands of wire do not come into contact with adjacent copper strips. As a safeguard, cut gaps in the copper strips wherever necessary to eliminate any possibility of the copper strips used by the main circuit from becoming 'live'.

The radio is switched by a low-voltage relay. Fig 3.15 shows the layout for a typical relay housed in a d.i.l. package. This is mounted on a separate board to keep it well away from mains

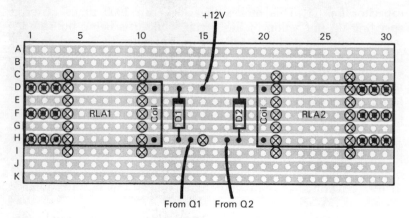

Figure 3.14 Project 12: mains relay board

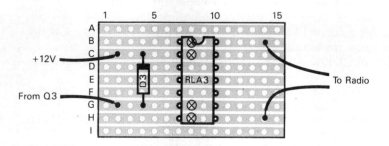

Figure 3.15 Project 12: radio-relay board

voltages. Before mounting this relay, check which terminals connect to the coil and contacts and, if necessary, modify the connection shown in the figure. The figure shows a protective diode (D3); certain types of relay already have the diode incorporated, in which case D3 may be omitted.

The three circuit-boards are mounted in the bottom of the enclosure (Fig 3.16). The main board and the board for RLA1 and RLA2 are mounted on horizontal hold-down strips (pcb guides). These are self-adhesive moulded plastic strips which grip the board by the edge and hold it a few millimetres away from the inner surface of the enclosure. The board for RLA3 is held in place by a double-sided adhesive pad, or a lump of Blu-tack.

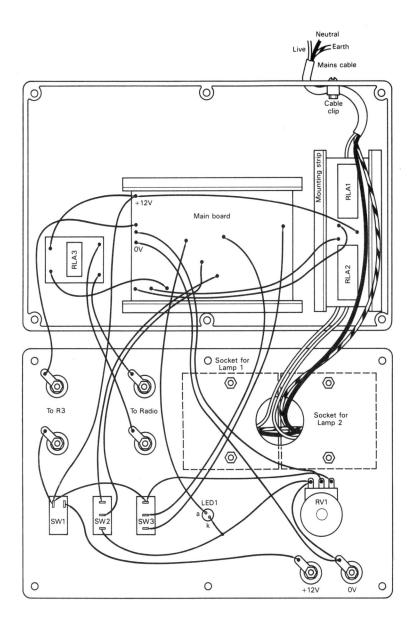

Figure 3.16 Project 12: arrangement of circuit boards and off-board wiring

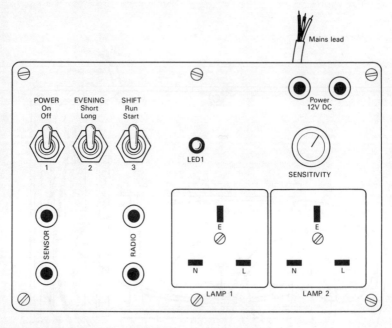

Figure 3.17 Project 12: stripboard layout of panel

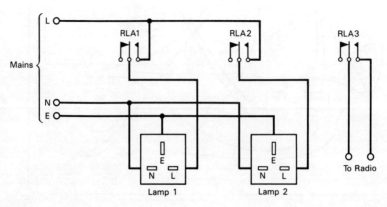

Figure 3.18 Relay circuits. Note that the mains sockets are drawn as seen from the front

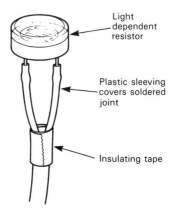

Light
dependent
resistor

Plastic sleeving
covers soldered
joint

Insulating tape

Figure 3.19 The light sensor

The switches, sockets and other off-board components are mounted on the lid (Fig 3.17). Cable suitable for mains current is used for wiring to the contacts of RLA1 and RLA2 (Fig 3.18). Although Fig 3.13 shows several leads running from the 0V and + 12V rails to various off-board components, it may be preferable to make direct connections from the 0V and +12V supply terminals instead.

R3 is fixed in the corner of a window, so that it receives natural daylight, even when the curtains are drawn together. It must not receive light from the lamps. It is connected to the panel by a light-duty lead, soldered to its terminal pins (Fig 3.19).

The radio set is controlled either by wiring the relay in series with its on/off switch or by by inserting a 'battery sandwich' (Fig 3.20) between two of the cells powering the set. In the first case the set is left with its switch off; in the second case it is left with its switch on. Remember that modifying the switching of the set may invalidate its guarantee. Alternatively, RLA3 is of the same type as the others, and a third mains socket is installed on the panel. A mains-powered radio or a TV is plugged into the socket and left with its power switch on.

When wiring is finished, check the mains connections very carefully. Test for short-circuits between each of the three mains lines and between the mains lines and the main circuit. Before substituting the 470μF capacitor for C1, let the circuit run for a while to confirm that it is operating correctly.

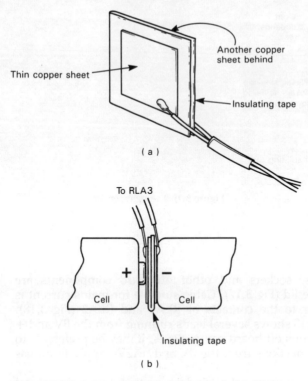

Thin copper sheet

Another copper
sheet behind

Insulating tape

(a)

To RLA3

+

Cell

—

Cell

Insulating tape

(b)

Figure 3.20 A battery sandwich (a) the sandwich (b) how to insert it between adjacent cells

Components required

Resistors (see p.139)

R1	330k
R2	820k
R3	ORP12 light-dependent resistor
R4	3k3
R5	100k
R6	820Ω
R7-R9	560Ω (3 off)
VR1	100k rotary carbon potentiometer

Capacitors

C1	470µ, electrolytic

Semiconductors
LED1   light-emitting diode
D1-D3   1N4148 silicon signal diode (3 off)
Q1-3   ZTX300 npn transistor (3 off)

Integrated circuits
IC1   7555 CMOS timer
IC2   4015BE CMOS dual 4-bit shift register
IC3,IC6   4011BE CMOS quadruple 2-input NAND gate (2 off)
IC4   4024BE CMOS 7-stage binary counter
IC5   4025BE CMOS triple 3-input NOR gate
IC7   CA3140 CMOS operational amplifier

Miscellaneous
SW1   SPST toggle switch
SW2,SW3   SPDT toggle switch (2 off)
RLA1, RLA2 12V relay 12V, coil resistance approx 200Ω, SPST or
SPDT contacts, contacts rated for 240V AC, up to 1A or more, pcb
mounting (2 off)
RLA3 12V miniature or sub-miniature relay, d.i.l. type or similar,
coil resistance approx 200Ω, SPST or SPDT contacts, contacts rated
for low voltage and current
3-pin 13A mains sockets, surface-mounting, unswitched
stripboard 23 strips by 37 holes, 11 strips by 30 holes, 9 strips by
15 holes
1mm terminal pins (20 off)
suitable plastic enclosure, approx 220mm x 150mm x 60mm
8-way d.i.l. sockets (2 off)
14-way d.i.l. sockets (5 off)
16-way d.i.l. socket
knob for VR1
4mm terminal sockets and plugs (1 red, 1 black, 2 yellow, 2 green
self-adhesive horizontal mounting strips or pcb guides (2 pcs
200mm long)
bolts and nuts for mounting mains sockets
cable clip, bolt and nut

Project 13 Tamper-proof audible warning device

One of the problems about any security installation is where to
locate the AWD. Several of the simpler projects in this book are
self-contained, with a small AWD in the same enclosure as the
circuit. The disadvantage of this is that, when the AWD is
triggered, the intruder can quickly locate the source of sound and

take steps to deactivate it. It is common practice to mount the AWD on the outside of the house, or in the loft. The difficulty then arises that the leads between the detector and the AWD are liable to be cut, rendering the system ineffective. This project shows how to overcome any attempt to tamper with the system by cutting the leads.

How it works

The AWD (which may be a low-power solid-state buzzer or a high-volume solid-state siren) is powered by its own battery. This and the circuit at the top of Fig 3.21 are housed in the same enclosure as the AWD. Current flowing through R1 could turn on Q1, causing the AWD to sound. However, a pair of leads runs from this circuit to a relay that is part of the detector circuit. This relay has its contacts normally *closed*, short-circuiting the emitter-base

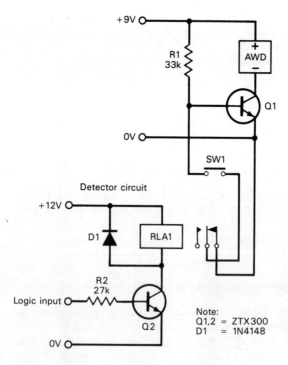

Figure 3.21 Project 13: Tamper-proof AWD

junction of the transistor. With its base at 0V, the transistor is off and the AWD does not sound.

When the relay is energised by the detector circuit turning on Q2, the relay contacts open, allowing current to flow to the base of Q1 and turning it on. The AWD sounds. Cutting the leads between the AWD housing and the detector has the same effect as opening the relay contacts; the AWD sounds. For the same reason, the alarm is sounded if the detector device fails, for example, if anyone switches off its power supply.

Many of the enclosures made for installing on the outside of a building incorporate a tamper-proof switch. The contacts of this are held together as long as the cover of the enclosure is bolted firmly in place. If an attempt is made to unscrew the cover to tamper with the contents of the enclosure, the contacts open. Such a switch is represented by SW1 in Fig 40. The AWD sounds as soon as someone tries to open its enclosure.

This project can be used as an enhancement of all the alarm projects in this book. In these, a transistor switch is used to turn on the AWD, when it receives a logic high. To adapt the circuit to the tamper proof alarm, simply replace the AWD of the original circuit by RLA1, as shown at the bottom left of Fig 3.21. The logic high turns on the transistor, energises the relay and causes its contacts to open. If the relay does not include its own protective diode, D1 is required in addition.

An alternative way of controlling the alarm is shown in Fig 3.22. This uses an opto coupler. A low logic level results in a current through the LED of the optocoupler. The light from the LED turns

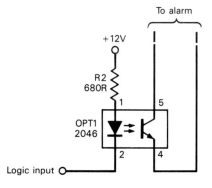

Figure 3.22 Project 13: alternative control by optocoupler

on the phototransistor, short-circuiting Q1 of the alarm circuit, and the alarm is silent. A logical high input turns off the LED, the phototransistor is turned off, and the alarm sounds.

Construction

Fig 2.23 shows the layout for both versions of the project. The layout on the board of the detector circuit may need to be modified depending on what space is available and the type of relay used. If there is no space on the main circuit board of the detector, the relay can be mounted on a separate piece of board.

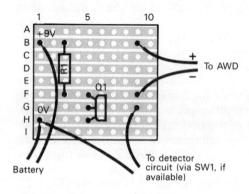

Figure 3.23 Project 13: stripboard layout

The circuit requires less than 0.3mA when quiescent so it should run for over 2 months, day and night, with a PP3 9V alkaline battery. Inspect the battery every 6-8 weeks of use, to check its condition.

Components required

Resistors (see p.139)
R1   33k

Semiconductors
D1   1N4148 silicon signal diode (if not present in relay)
Q1   ZTX300 npn transistor

Miscellaneous
OPT1 2046 single optocoupler, or ultra-miniature pcb mounting relay with change-over contacts

stripboard 95mm × 63mm, 63mm × 25mm
1mm terminal pins (4 off)
PP3 battery connector

Project 14 Infra-red intruder detector

Like Project 2, this device depends for its action on a beam of light being broken when the intruder passes in front of the sensor. In this project we use a beam of infra-red radiation. The device works in complete darkness, if necessary, and the beam is invisible to an intruder. However, the system works well in daylight or in artificial light, provided that the sensor is not saturated by having a bright light shining directly on it.

This project has a range of several metres, particularly under low-light or in darkness, so is suitable for protecting a large room.

How it works
The infra-red radiation is produced from a bank of three high-energy infra-red LEDs. The beam consists of a series of pulses 0.1 milliseconds long, produced at the rate of 500 pulses per second. When the LEDs are switched on, the current through each of them is 700mA, giving a brief but very high intensity flash. This is detectable at a much greater distance than would be the radiation from the same LEDs operating at their maximum continuous current of 100mA. The LEDs are actually passing current for only 5% of the time, and so the *average* current through each LED is only 35mA.

Using an intermittent beam has another advantage. The beam frequency is 500Hz and it is possible to use a receiver circuit tuned to respond only to signals close to the same frequency. This means that one common intermittent source of infra-red, the light emitted from filament lamps, with an imposed frequency of 50Hz from the mains, has negligible effect on the receiver.

The circuit consists of two separate circuits, the transmitter and the receiver. The transmitter circuit (Fig 3.24) uses a 7555 ic to produce the required waveform. However, the 7555 timer output is necessarily high for longer than it is low. This is because C1 charges (output high) through R1 *and* R2, but discharges (output low) only through R2. For this reason we use a NAND gate, with its inputs wired together to invert the timer signal.

The inverted signal, high for 0.1ms, low for 1.9ms is fed to a

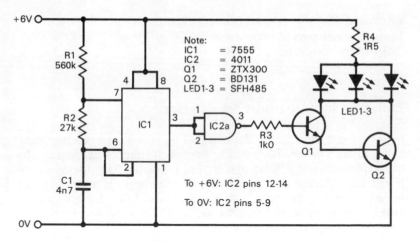

Figure 3.24 Infra-red intruder detector; transmitter

Darlington pair of transistors, acting as a switch to turn the LEDs on and off. Only a very low-value resistor (1.5Ω) is required in series with the LEDs. Note that this circuit operates on a 6V supply and must not be run at a higher voltage without increasing the value of R4.

The receiver circuit has a 4.5V power supply; it can be operated at 5V too, but not higher, as the supply to IC3 must be between 4V and 5.25V. The sensor is a phototransistor (Fig 3.25) spectrally matched to the LEDs of the transmitter. It has collector and emitter terminals but no base terminal. IC3 is an amplifier specially designed for operating with infra-red signals. The output of the amplifier at pin 1 goes to a high-pass filter (C6,R8) to reduce the strength of signals below 400Hz, including mains frequency from filament lamps. IC4 is a tone decoder ic, the action of which is based on a phase locked loop. It incorporates its own oscillator, set to 500Hz by selection of C7 and R9. This is known as the *central frequency*. The output of the ic (pin 8) is normally high, but goes low whenever a signal close to the central frequency is being received at sufficient strength. The tone decoder responds to a suitable signal even in the presence of a considerable amount of noise. This gives the device immunity from interference by 'noise' resulting from other sources of infra-red in the room.

The output of the tone decoder goes to a flip-flop made from two NOR gates. The flip-flop is reset by pressing SW1 and its

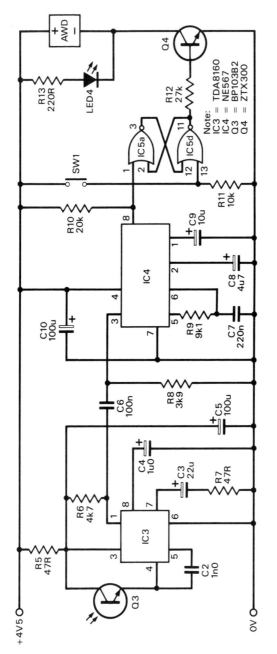

Figure 3.25 Project 14: infra-red intruder detector; receiver

output at pin 11 goes low. As long as the infra-red beam remains unbroken, the output of IC4 remains high. As soon as the beam is broken, the output of IC4 goes low, setting the flip-flop. Pin 11 goes high, turning on Q4. LED4 lights and the AWD sounds. As with other alarm circuits, the AWD can be replaced by a relay or optocoupler (see p. 95).

Constructing the transmitter

The circuit has a compact layout (Fig 3.26) so that the transmitter can be made as inconspicuous as possible. It fits into a small enclosure with an aperture cut in one side to produce the beam of radiation. The circuit requires 130mA, which means that it is best powered from a 6V mains adaptor. If batteries are preferred, four 'D' type alkaline cells will last approximately 100 hours, but these would be suitable for a system used only occasionally.

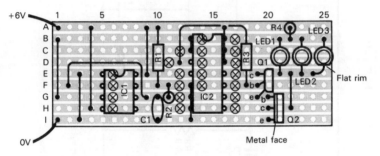

Figure 3.26 Project 14: stripboard layout of transmitter

Assemble IC1 and IC2 first, before connecting the LEDs, and check that the two ics are operating properly. The correct operation of the circuit is most conveniently tested with an oscilloscope. Without such an instrument, the easiest way of checking that the oscillator is working is to use a crystal earphone.

Connect one terminal of this to the 0V line and the other to a 100n capacitor. Connect the other terminal of the capacitor to pin 3 of IC1. A crisp tone of frequency 500Hz (a little below middle C on the piano) is heard. This can also be heard if the capacitor terminal is connected to either end of R3. Now add the LEDs, making sure they they are connected the right way round, with their cathodes (indicated by a 'flat' on the rim) toward the lower edge of the board. With an earphone, the 500Hz tone can now be heard if the capacitor is connected to either the anode or cathode terminals of the LEDs. In the dark, a dull red glow can be seen in the centre of each LED.

If an oscilloscope is used, the voltage at the anodes of the LEDs (i.e. where they connect to R4) is 6V, dropping to about 3V for 100ms at 500Hz. This shows that the forward voltage drop across the LEDs is about 2.8V when they are carrying 700mA each.

As the LEDs are mounted in Fig 3.26, the beam is perpendicular to the plane of the circuit board. The leads of the LEDs can be bent to direct the beam in other directions if required. Take care that the leads to not touch each other.

Constructing the receiver

The receiver requires only 15mA when quiescent, so battery operation is feasible. It can be run from *three* type AA alkaline cells for over 100 hours, and for about 800 hours if D cells are used. Alternatively, use a 4.5V mains adaptor. Although most solid-state AWDs or sirens will operate on 4.5V, the volume of sound may not be adequate. It is worth considering the use of the tamper-proof alarm (Project 13) since this has its own power source, with higher voltage. In that case, a relay or optocoupler is substituted for the AWD shown in Fig 3.25.

First assemble the sensor and amplifier circuits (Q3, IC3, C2-C5, R5-R7). Note that the collector of Q3 is indicated by the flat on its rim and that this lies toward the *upper* edge of the board (Fig 3.27). The layout shows the phototransistor orientated so as to receive a beam arriving perpendicular to the board. The leads can be bent to point it in other directions.

Test the circuit by switching on the transmitter and holding it a metre or more from the receiver, with its LEDs aimed at the phototransistor. An oscilloscope shows that the 500Hz signal is coming from pin 1. This signal can be heard if an earphone is connected to pin 1, as described above.

Now assemble the high-pass filter and tone decoder circuit (IC4, C6 to C10, R8-R10). Note that C10 is to be connected with its leads as close as possible to the power terminals (pins 4 and 7) of IC4. Connect a voltmeter to IC4 pin 8. The output is low (0V) when the transmitter is switched off, but goes high (4.5V) when the transmitter is on and its beam reaches the phototransistor.

Test the system with the receiver on one side of the room and the transmitter on the other side of the room, 3 to 4 metres away. It responds in daylight, artificial light or darkness provided that the bright sunlight or artificial light are not directed straight at the

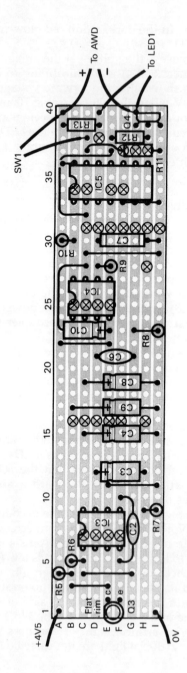

Figure 3.27 Project 14: stripboard layout of the receiver

phototransistor. However, the range is greater in darkness or semi-darkness.

The transmitter is enclosed in a plastic box with the LED and push-button SW1 mounted on the lid. If the device is to be operated under brighter conditions, the board is best situated at the rear of the enclosure, with an aperture cut in the lid. This narrows the field of view of the phototransistor and helps to ensure that extraneous sources of infra-red do not affect it.

Installing the detector

The receiver and transmitter should be mounted on opposite sides of a room, or in opposite corners if this is more convenient. If the device is being mounted in a long narrow room or hallway, it is preferable that the beam slants diagonally across the area. This means that an intruder passing along the hallway will spend relatively longer in the beam, making detection more certain. It is also possible to make use of a mirror, so that the transmitter and receiver can be on the same side of the room.

If the transmitter and receiver are mounted about 1m above floor level this makes it difficult for an intruder to 'step over' the beam, yet allows pets to pass underneath it. A pressure mat (Project 3) could guard against an intruder spotting the transmitter and crawling under the beam. If the transmitter and receiver are concealed, the intruder will be unaware of their existence until too late. There is no problem in disguising the units, either by building them into the furniture or making them look like harmless objects, such as books, or by standing a potted plant on them.

When the transmitter and receiver are in position and aligned, switch on the power. The LED usually comes on and the AWD sounds, if connected. The LED can be extinguished and the AWD silenced by pressing SW2 (assuming that you are not standing between the transmitter and receiver !). The system is now active; as soon as the beam is broken the LED lights and the AWD sounds.

Components required
Resistors (see p.139)

R1	560k
R2,R12	27k (2 off)
R3	1k
R4	1.5Ω
R5, R7	47Ω (2 off)
R8	3k9
R9	9k1

R10	20k
R11	10k
R13	220Ω

Capacitors

C1	4n7 metallised ceramic
C2	1n polystyrene
C3	22µ electrolytic
C4	1µ electrolytic
C5,C10	100µ electrolytic (2 off)
C6	100n polyester
C7	220n polyester layer
C8	4µ7 electrolytic
C9	10µ electrolytic

Semiconductors

LED1-LED3	SFH485 GaAlAs infra-red emitter (3 off)
LED4	light-emitting diode
Q1,Q4	ZTX300 npn transistor (2 off)
Q2	BD131 npn power transistor
Q3	BP103B2 silicon infra-red phototransistor

Integrated circuits

IC1	7555 CMOS timer
IC2	4011BE CMOS quadruple 2-input NAND gate
IC3	TDA8160 infra-red remote control amplifier
IC4	NE567 tone decoder/phase locked loop
IC5	4001BE CMOS quadruple 2-input NOR gate

Miscellaneous

S1   push-to-make push-button
stripboard 9 strips by 25 holes, 9 strips by 40 holes
1mm terminal pins (8 off)
suitable plastic enclosures
8-way d.i.l. sockets (3 off)
14-way d.i.l. sockets (2 off)

4 Protection against other hazards

Project 15 Fire detector alarm (smoke)

A simple fire alarm was described in Chapter 2. This depends on detecting an excessive temperature. Fire produces smoke as well as heat and this gives us another way of fire detection. The advantages of a smoke detector are that many kinds of substance smoulder and produce copious quantities of smoke long before eventually bursting into flame. In such circumstances, smoke detection may give an early warning that a serious fire is imminent. A second advantage is that smoke usually spreads widely.

If it is suitable sited, the detector can monitor a very large area of a building. The detector is placed high in the room, or at the top of a stair-well, where the first smoke is likely to accumulate. One possible disadvantage of the smoke detector is that some inflammable substances burn without producing appreciable smoke.

How it works
The action of the circuit depends upon the scattering of light by the particles of smoke. The sensor is a photo-transistor, enclosed in a smoke cell. The smoke cell is a box which smoke can freely enter. The channel though which the smoke drifts has bends in it to prevent light from outside reaching the photo-transistor. There is also a light-emitting diode in the smoke cell. Light from the LED can not reach the photo-transistor directly because there is a screen between them. The walls of the channel are matt black, reflecting very little of the light from the LED. In this way the photo-transistor is normally in almost complete darkness. When smoke enters the cell it scatters the light coming from the LED and some

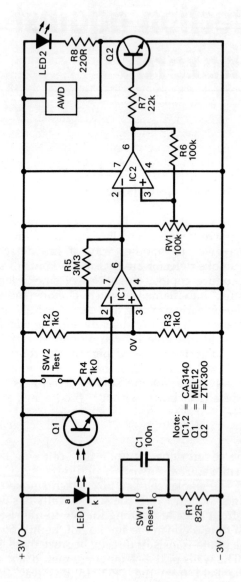

Figure 4.1 Project 15: smoke detector

of this scattered light reaches the photo-transistor. The detection of scattered light triggers the alarm circuit.

LED1 (Fig 4.1) is a high-intensity red light-emitting diode. The value of R1 is low, so the current is approximately 50mA and the light intensity 200mcd. There is a push-to-break button in series with LED1 to extinguish it and reset the circuit. The photo-transistor, although shown in Fig 4.2 as a single transistor, is a photo-Darlington with two transistors connected as a Darlington pair to obtain very high gain. Q1 has a base terminal but this is not used in this circuit, and is not shown in the drawing. The amount of current flowing through Q1 is zero in complete darkness but increases with increasing light intensity.

The operational amplifier IC1 is connected as a current-to-voltage converter. Its output V_{OUT} is given by:

$$V_{OUT} = -iR$$

where i is the current from Q1 and R is the resistance of R5. When there is no smoke in the cell, V_{OUT} is about $-0.7V$, corresponding to a current of $0.2\mu A$. When smoke enters the cell, the current increases to double this amount or more, and V_{OUT} falls accordingly.

When referring to output voltages we are considering the operational amplifiers to be working on a split supply, $\pm 3V$, provided by a 6V battery. The voltage at the (+) input of IC1 is 0V, obtained by the potential divider of two equal resistors, R2 and R3.

The output from IC1 goes to the inverting input of IC2. This is acting as a comparator with a trigger action. The voltage at the (+) input of IC2 is set by adjusting RV1 so that it is between $-0.8V$ and $-0.9V$. Since the (+) input is at a lower voltage than the (−) input, the output of IC2 swings down to $-3V$. In this state, Q2 is off and no current passes through the indicator LED2, or the AWD.

When there is smoke in the cell, the output of IC1 falls, bringing the voltage at the (−) input of IC2 *below* that at the (+) input. The ouput of IC2 swings rapidly positive. This turns on Q2, causing the indicator to light and the alarm to sound. Once the circuit has been triggered, the positive voltage at the output of IC2 pulls up the voltage at its (+) input to about 0.3V. This is positive feedback. Once this has happened, any slight rise in the output from IC1, such as might be caused by temporary clearing of the smoke, is insufficient to reverse the action. The alarm continues to sound.

As explained above, clearing the smoke from the cell does not turn off the alarm. The circuit is reset by pressing SW1 to extinguish LED1. In complete darkness the output of IC1 rises above the voltage at the (+) input of IC2 and the output of the ic falls.

The circuit also incorporates a test facility. This is important since it is possible that the LED may burn out without the user becoming aware of this happening. When the test button is pressed briefly, the current that flows through R4 trips the circuit as if smoke is present. The indicator LED comes on, confirming that the circuit (apart from LED1 and Q1) is operating correctly. To complete the test, the reset button is pressed. The fact that the indicator LED goes out shows that LED1 is still functioning and that Q1 is detecting the light coming from it.

Construction
The circuit, with the possible excepton of the AWD, is to be mounted high in the room and in what will probably be a conspicuous place. For this reason the circuit layout (Figs 4.2 and 4.3) is made as compact as possible and the project can be housed in a small case. The smoke cell fits in one end of the case.

Fig 4.4 shows how to make a smoke cell from thin matt black card. The cell has openings in its lower and upper sides to allow the smoke to enter and leave. Within the cell, the path of the smoke consists of a double-ended light trap.

Smoke enters at the bottom, rising naturally by convection and passes along the channel consisting of the lower third of the cell (Fig 4.4(d)). At the right-hand end it passes around the edge of the partition and passes toward the left, along the middle third of the cell. Here are situated the LED and the photo-transistor. There are two holes in the side of the box for these, and there is a small shield between them. When it reaches the left end the smoke passes up into the top third of the cell. It then flows toward the right and leaves the cell by the opening in the top surface.

The dimensions in Fig 4.4 (in millimetres) are for a cell intended to fit into an abs plastic case of external dimensions 120mm x 65mm × 40mm. Fold the outer case into the correct shape and glue the tabs, except for those on the top of the box. Glue the lower partition in place, leaving a gap on the right. Glue the upper partition in place, leaving a gap on the left. Fold over and glue the top of the box to the sides.

The bottom and lid of the case have a row of 6mm holes drilled in them to allow smoke to enter and leave the cell (Fig 4.5(a)). The walls of the case are grooved to hold the circuit boards. Board A (Fig 4.2) holds the LED and photo-transistor. These are positioned

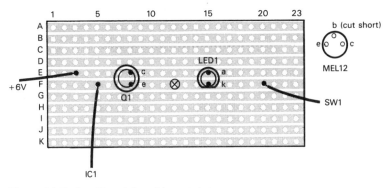

Figure 4.2 Project 15: stripboard layout A

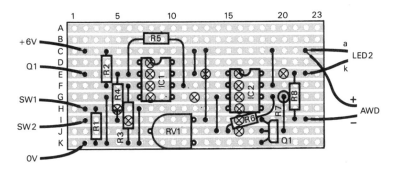

Figure 4.3 Project 15: stripboard layout B

so as to fit neatly into the two holes in the cell when the board is in its groove close to one side of the cell.

Board B (Fig 4.3) holds the remainder of the circuit, except for the AWD. It is best to assemble both boards and complete the off-board wiring before testing the circuit. Mount SW1, and LED2 on the wall of the case. C1 is soldered directly to the terminals of SW1. The connections to the AWD can be left until testing is complete. With the cell and both boards in the case, place the lid over the cell end of the case, leaving the circuit-board uncovered for testing.

Test voltages are measured with reference to the 0V present at the (+) input of IC1. Connect one lead of the testmeter to this point (or to the exposed wire lead of R2 or R3). Unless your meter has automatic polarity, connect the positive probe to this point and the negative probe to the test point. With LED1 on, the output of IC1

79

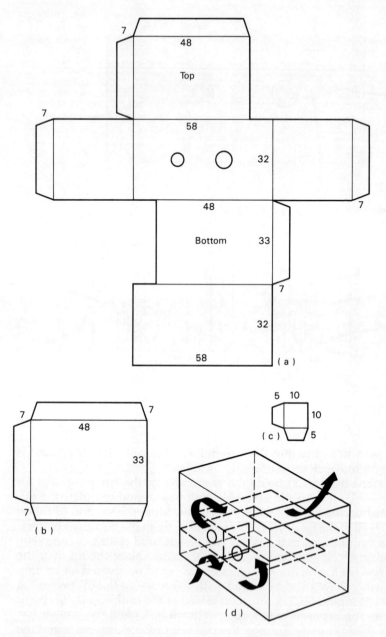

Figure 4.4 Smoke cell (a) outer case (b) partition (c) screen (d) perspective

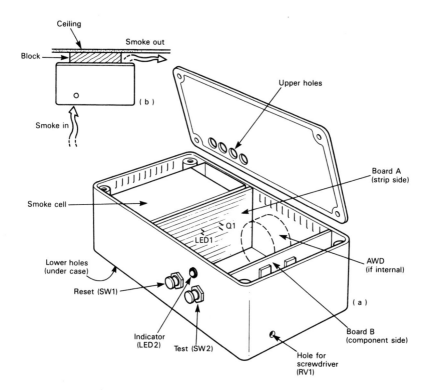

Figure 4.5 Project 15: the completed project

(at pin 6) is slightly negative, probably about −0.7V. The exact value depends upon the gain of Q1 and how much light it is receiving from LED1.

Press SW1; V$_{OUT}$ is very close to 0V. Now check the (+) input of IC2. Turn RV1 fully anticlockwise; the voltage at (+) is close to −3V. LED2 is out. As you turn VR1 slowly clockwise the voltage slowly increases. As soon as the voltage just exceeds that at the other input (from IC1) there is a sudden upward jump and LED2 comes on. The output of IC2 has swung slightly positive.

If the AWD is a small solid-state sounder, it can be housed in the case. However, it is usually the function of a smoke detector to provide surveillance in a part of the premises that is unoccupied. The AWD is therefore best located in a more frequently used part of the house, where is it is more likely to be heard. This project

81

can also be incorporated into a domestic system, as described in the final section of this chapter.

The circuit requires about 60mA, mainly to supply the 50mA required for LED1. Fire detection devices are normally run for 24 hours of the day, so the most suitable power supply is a 6V dc mains adaptor.

Smoke test

Close the case and adjust the triggering level of the circuit as follows. Insert a fine screwdriver through the hole in the case and engage RV1. Switch on the power supply. Turn RV1 anticlockwise until the indicator LED goes out. Then slowly turn RV1 clockwise, pressing the test button repeatedly. Stop when LED2 comes on and stays on. Pressing the reset button puts LED2 out. If it does not go out, you have turned RV1 too far. Turn it anticlockwise and try again, turning it more slowly this time.

Rest the project on the workbench, overhanging one edge so that smoke can enter the lower apertures. Press the reset button if the indicator is lit. Hold a source of smoke below the device; use a roll of smouldering corrugated cardboard, smoky oil-lamp, or a candle with a coin held over its wick to make it smoke. The indicator lights (and the AWD sounds, if connected) within a few tens of seconds of the smoke entering the cell.

Take care not tó start a fire while testing; dispose safely of all smouldering materials and spent matches.

Setting up

Mount the completed project as near the ceiling as possible. If it is mounted on the ceiling, use a block slightly smaller than the case (Fig 4.5(b)) so that smoke can pass through the cell and out through the upper openings. Although the smoke cell is proof against ordinary levels of illumination, the device should be mounted where it will not receive direct illumination from sunlight or from a lighting fitting close by. Switch on the power supply and check the setting of RV1 as described above.

Components required

Resistors (see p.139)

R1	82Ω
R2-R4	1k (3 off)
R5	3M3
R6	100k
R7	22k

R8   220Ω
RV1   100k miniature horizontal preset potentiometer

Capacitor
C1   100n polyester

Semiconductors
LED1   High-intensity (200mcd or more) red LED
LED2   green LED
Q1   MEL12 photo-Darlington
Q2   ZTX300 npn transistor

Integrated circuits
IC1,IC2   CA3140 CMOS operational amplifier (2 off)

Miscellaneous
S1   push-to-break push-button
S2   push-to-make push-button
stripboard, 2 pieces, 11 strips by 23 holes (or longer, to fit grooves in case)
1mm terminal pins (11 off)
suitable plastic enclosure
audible warning device
8-way d.i.l. sockets (2 off)
thin matt black card for making smoke cell

Project 16 Frost alarm

The circuit warns the householder if frost is imminent. There is then time to take action to avoid frost damage such as switching on a heater, checking that no taps have been left dripping into the sink or washbasin, and possibly covering some of the more tender garden plants. Readers with sufficient experience of electronics construction can adapt this project to switch on a heater automatically, as explained later.

The alarm sub-circuit in this project gives out a distinctive two-tone sound. It is not loud enough to rouse the neighbours so, while it is not suitable for a major security system, it can be used with other security circuits such as the fire and flood alarms, or when one of the security devices is being used to secure the safety of an invalid or elderly person.

How it works
The sensing section of the circuit (Fig 4.6) employs a thermistor. It is very similar to the fire alarm, Project 7, but operates in the

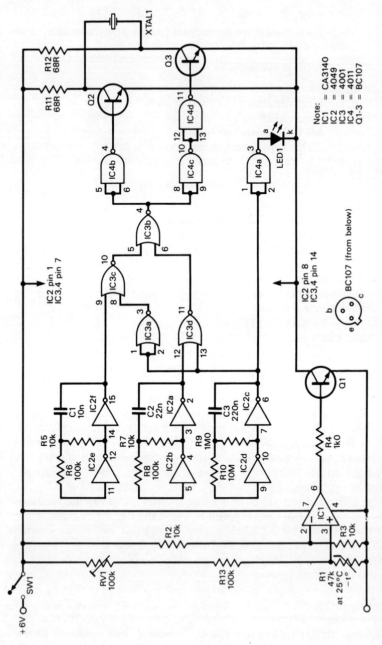

Figure 4.6 Project 16: frost alarm circuit

reverse sense. That is to say, the output of the amplifier goes high when the temperature of R1 falls *below* a given level. As in Project 7, an operational amplifier is used as a comparator, but the fixed voltage is applied to the (−) input and the temperature-dependent varying voltage goes to the (+) input.

R2 and R3 are equal, so the voltage at the (−) input is 3V. The resistance of R1 is less than 100kΩ at temperatures above 10°C , so the voltage at the (+) input is less than 3V. The amplifier output is 0V and Q1 is off. As temperature falls, the resistance increases and the voltage at the (+) input rises. The setting of RV1 is such that the voltage rises to 3V at the danger temperature. This is a temperature a little above freezing point, say 3°C, to give advance warning of frost and to allow for R1 not necessarily being at the coldest point in the vicinity.

As the temperature falls below the danger point, the voltage at the (+) input rises above 3V. The output of the amplifier rises to 4V, turning on Q1. Current now flows through the alarm-generating sub-circuit. Note that, in contrast with Project 7, the amplifier does not have a feedback resistor. This is because the alarm is to sound only for as long as the temperature is below the danger level. If the temperature rises again, the alarm is to be silenced.

The alarm-generating sub-circuit is based on three astable multivibrators, each consisting of two INVERT gates. The six gates required are all contained in a single ic (IC2). The astables operate at three different frequencies, determined by the timing capacitors (C1, C2 and C3) and the timing resistors (R5, R7 and R9). The frequency of this type of astable is given by:

$$f = \frac{1}{2.2RC}$$

Using this equation, we find that the frequencies are 4.5kHz, 2kHz, and 2Hz respectively, running down the astables in Fig 4.6 from top to bottom. The two higher frequencies produce the two audible tones, while the lower frequency is used to switch from one tone to the other.

The outputs of the two audio-frequency astables go to two NOR gates (IC3).

The other inputs of these gates receive either the signal or the inverted signal from the slow astable. The result is that the audio signals are passed through one gate or the other alternately. The final NOR gate combines the outputs from the two gates, so that a two-tone signal is produced.

The two-tone signal then goes to a pair of transistors. It passes through one INVERT gate (we use a NAND gate of IC4 with its inputs wired together) on its way to Q2, and through two INVERT gates on its way to Q3. Thus Q2 and Q3 act in the opposite sense; when one is on the other is off. When Q2 is on and Q3 is off, The collector of Q2 is at about 1V and that of Q3 is at 6V. The voltage across the piezo crystal XTAL1 is 5V.

When Q2 is off and Q3 is on, the voltage across the crystal is again 5V but in the opposite direction. This alternating voltage causes the crystal to vibrate strongly and the signal is converted into sound.

The crystal used in this project is a thin circular slice of piezo-electric material mounted on a brass disc of slightly larger diameter. The material is usually supplied with wires already soldered to the disc and its silvered upper surface. If wires are not provided take special care when soldering to the silvered layer. Use a hot iron but let it touch the silvered layer for only a second or two, otherwise the layer may be damaged.

The fourth NAND gate of IC4 is used as an inverter-buffer to drive LED1. This is driven by the slow astable and flashes at 2Hz whenever the alarm is sounding.

This alarm sub-circuit is a self-contained circuit module that can be used in connection with other projects. The final stage of most alarm projects is a transistor which switches on a solid-state AWD. The AWD can be replaced by the alarm sub-circuit of this project, consisting of IC2-IC4, their associated resistors and capacitors, XTAL1 and LED1.

The alarm sub-circuit can be replaced by a relay, as shown on p. 96. This could be a low-voltage relay wired so as to switch an external AWD, or one of the devices on the loop of a full-scale domestic system as described in Chapters 5 to 7.

Another possibility is to use a relay capable of switching mains current. The relay can is then be used to switch on an electric heater automatically. Alternatively, the relay could switch current through a heating tape to provide a low-level of heating to prevent freezing of pipes in a cupboard, for example, or to prevent frost damage to hot-house plants. Care must be taken when constructing such a circuit, since the current taken by an electric heater is considerable. Also one must be sure that the heater is not capable of causing a fire. Consider the possible effects of having the heater switched on for long periods in a confined space. It must not be possible for inflammable materials to fall on to the unattended heater. Adapting the project for automatic heating is only for the most experienced persons. You should seek expert advice if you have any doubt whatever on how to set about it.

Construction

First build the astable multivibrators, IC2 and associated components (Fig 4.7). Connect the power supply to the terminal at A1 and (temporarily) to Q20. The output of each astable is monitored using an oscilloscope or you can listen to the output using an earphone, as described on p. 70. From the audio-frequency astables you hear a high tone and a lower one. From the slow astable you hear sharp clicks twice a second.

Next assemble the logic circuits (IC3, IC4, Q2, Q3 etc). A two-tone signal is produced at pin 4 of IC3, at pins 4, 10 and 11 of IC4 and at the collectors of Q2 and Q3. The volume of sound from the crystal is very low until it is properly mounted.

Build the sensor sub-circuit, consisting of IC1 and its associated resistors. The thermistor R1 is connected on a long lead and eventually mounted outdoors in an area exposed to frosts. With SW1 connected to 0V, the output of IC1 is low (0V) at room temperatures down to about 10°C. To test the circuit, surround R1 with cubes of ice and leave it for a minute. Then it is possible to set RV1 so that the output of IC1 rises to about 4V. When R1 is removed from the ice, the output falls to 0V after a few seconds.

Complete the cuircuit by adding R4 and Q1. When R1 is placed at a near-freezing temperature, the alarm sounds and the LED flashes.

The circuit is enclosed in a suitable plastic container, which also houses the battery. Since the circuit requires less than 2mA when quiescent, a battery of 4 AA cells in a battery box is a suitable power supply. Mount the power switch SW1 and the diode LED1 on the wall of the case. XTAL1 must be firmly mounted on the wall of the case (Fig 4.8). It is gripped by its rim but the greater part of the disc is free to vibrate. A firm mounting considerably increases the volume of sound produced.

Components required

Resistors (see p.139)
R1   bead thermistor, 47k at 25°C
R2,R3,R5,R7 10k (4 off)
R4   1k
R6,R8,R13   100k (3 off)

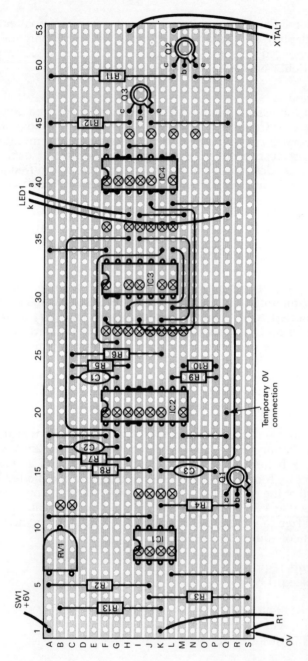

Figure 4.7 Project 16: stripboard layout

88

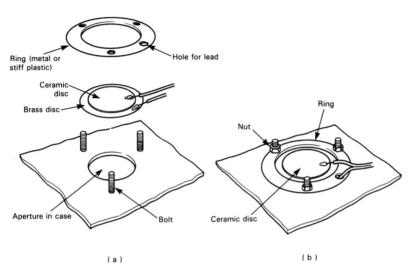

Ring (metal or
stiff plastic)

Hole for lead

Ceramic
disc

Brass disc

Ring

Nut

Aperture in case

Bolt

Ceramic disc

(a)

(b)

Figure 4.8 Mounting the transducer (a) exploded view (b) the mounted transducer

R9	1M
R10	10M
R11,R12	68Ω (2 off)
RV1	100k miniature horizontal preset resistor

Capacitors
C1	10n polyester
C2	22n polyester
C3	220n polyester

Semiconductors
LED1	high-intensity red light-emitting diode
Q1-Q3	BC107 npn transistor (3 off)

Integrated circuits
IC1	CA3140 CMOS operational amplifier
IC2	4049BE CMOS hex inverting buffer
IC3	4001BE CMOS quadruple NOR gate
IC4	4011BE CMOS quadruple NAND gate

Miscellaneous
XTAL1	ceramic piezo transducer (27mm preferred)
SW1	single-pole single-throw toggle switch

stripboard 19 strips by 53 holes

1mm terminal pins (6 off)
suitable plastic enclosure
8-way d.i.l. socket
14-way d.i.l. sockets (2 off)
16-way d.i.l. socket
6V battery box (4 × AA)
PP3 battery clip
nuts and bolts for mounting XTAL1

Project 17 Gas alarm

A slow leakage of inflammable gas such as butane can gradually
build up until the mixture with air is potentially explosive. Then a
small spark, such as that produced in an electric switch, or a
glowing cigarette end, or the presence of a naked flame, can
initiate a devastating explosion. This project is designed to detect
the presence of low levels of butane and several other commonly
occurring flammable gases and sound the alarm. Gases to which
it is sensitive include butane, iso-butane, propane, liquefied
petroleum gas, methane, natural gas, town gas, hydrogen and
ethanol vapour.

How it works
The action of the circuit depends upon a special gas sensor. This
consists of a coil of fine platinum wire covered with materials
which catalyse the oxidation of flammable gases. The sensor is
operated with a relatively large current passing through the coil to
bring it to a temperature of about 350°C. In the presence of the gas,
the heat produced as a result of oxidation raises the temperature
of the coil further. This raises its resistance, a change that can be
detected electronically. In order that there is no risk of the sensor
igniting the gas and causing an explosion, the coil is housed in a
dome of double-meshed stainless steel wire.

The temperature and therefore the resistance of the sensor coil
is also affected by factors other than the amount of flammable gas
present. These include the amount of current passing through the
coil, the ambient temperature, the atmospheric humidity and the
presence of other gases which react with the coating on the
platinum wire. To eliminate these effects, the circuit also includes
a similar coil, the compensator, which reacts in an identical way
to all factors, except the presence of flammable gases.

As shown in Fig 4.9, the sensor (R4) and the compensator (R5)

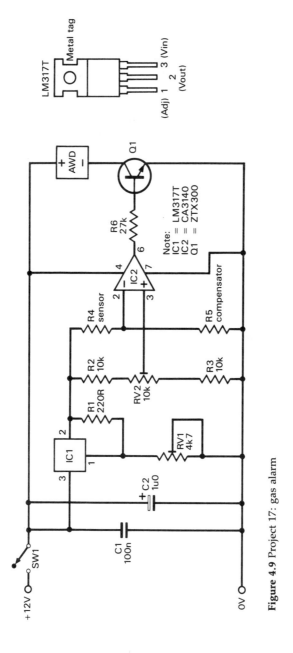

Figure 4.9 Project 17: gas alarm

are wired into a bridge circuit. The other two resistors in the bridge are R2 and R3. These are linked by a variable resistor RV2, used to balance the bridge.

The bridge is balanced by setting RV2 so that the voltage at the wiper of RV2 is a few millivolts less than that at the junction between the sensor and compensator. These voltages are compared by IC2, connected as a comparator. With its (+) input at a slightly lower voltage than its (−) input, the output of IC1 is 0V. The transistor Q1 is off and the AWD is silent.

We have said that the bridge is balanced but, as the description above makes clear, it is very slightly unbalanced. It is poised ready to be *un*balanced in the opposite direction by the presence of gas around the sensor. Changes of current through the bridge, changes in ambient temperature and other changes that affect both the sensor and the compensator have no effect on the balance (or slight lack of balance) of the bridge. But, when flammable gas is present, the oxidation of this in the sensor, and the consequent rise in sensor temperature tips the balance of the bridge. As the sensor resistance increases, the voltage at the (−) input of IC2 falls below that at the (+) input. The output of the amplifier swings sharply upward, turning on Q1 and sounding the alarm. It remains sounding until the gas has cleared.

The current to the bridge is supplied from a voltage regulator. IC1 is an adjustable voltage regulator with a maximum output current of 1.5A. The voltage supplied to the bridge is adjusted to 2.2V (±10%) by setting RV1.

Construction

This project requires about 400mA, so a mains adaptor providing at least 400mA at 12V dc is required. Note that the cheaper mains adaptors are usually rated at only 300mA and are unsuitable for this project.

Begin by assembling the voltage regulator sub-circuit, consisting of R1, RV1, C1, C2 and IC1 (Fig 4.10). Fit a medium-sized heat sink to IC1. Measure the output voltage at pin 2 of the ic and adjust RV1 until it is 2.2V. It is essential to set the voltage correctly at this stage, since over-voltage can burn out the sensor and compensator very quickly.

Assemble the remainder of the circuit. The sensor (R4) and compensator (R5) can be mounted on the outside of the case or fixed in a suitable position in the room, but do not connect them to the circuit yet. The sensor and compensator are sometimes both included in a single 4-pin unit, but normally they are sold as a

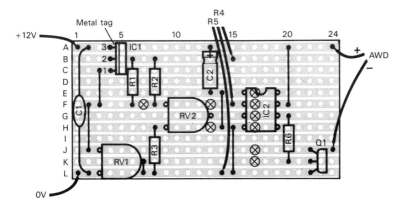

Figure 4.10 Project 17: stripboard layout of gas alarm

matched pair of units. The compensator is usually indicated by having a blue spot of paint on it.

Since most flammable gases are denser than air, R4 and R5 (or the project itself, if they are mounted on its case) should be as low as possible in the room. Fig 4.11 shows R4 and R5 soldered to a small piece of stripboard. The holes in the board may need to be drilled to a larger diameter to accommodate the pins of the resistors. The board has two holes for screwing it or bolting it in position, on the skirting, for example.

If the resistors are to be mounted on the project case, prepare the board as in Fig 4.11 but without the holes; do not solder in the resistors yet. Insert the terminal pins from the component side of

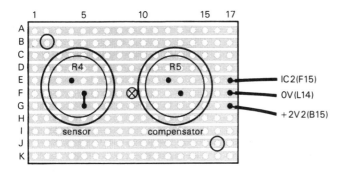

Figure 4.11 Mounting the sensor and compensator

the board, so that these pins project on the *strip* side of the board. Then bore pairs of holes in the wall of the case, spaced to take the resistor pins. Push the resistor pins through these holes so that the domes rest against the outside of the wall with their pins projecting through the holes into the interior. Push the board over the pins, tight against the inside of the wall, and solder the pins to the board. This holds the domes firmly in position.

Before connecting R4 and R5 to the circuit, try a dummy run with ordinary fixed resistors wired in place of them. A pair of 10Ω, ½W resistors are suitable, but note that these will become hot when current is switched on. Measure the voltage at the ends of these resistors; it is 2.2V at the 'top' of the bridge, 0V at the 'bottom' and about 1.1V at the junction of the two resistors. Check the wiring and the setting of RV1 if these voltages are not found. Adjust RV2 so that the voltage at the (+) input of IC2 is 1V, i.e. less than that at the (−) input. The output is 0V . Re-adjust RV2 to increase the voltage at the (+) input to about 1.2V. The output swings to 10V. Remove the 10Ω resistors and connect R4 and R5 into the circuit.

In Fig 4.10 the AWD is not mounted on the circuit board; it can be mounted externally or on the wall of the case. If preferred, the board can be cut longer (34 holes) to make room for a small AWD on the board, as in Fig 2.4.

Setting up

Switch on the power and allow about 30 seconds for the sensor and compensator to warm up and become stable. If the sensor and compensator are new, there will probably be a slight scorching smell at this stage, but this is normal. If the AWD is sounding, turn RV2 to silence it.

When the sensor and compensator are stable, adjust RV1 so that the voltage at the (+) input is about 20mV below that at the (−) input. Test the operation of the circuit by exposing the sensor and compensator to flammable gas. Sources of gas include: a piece of paper tissue soaked in ethanol or in petrol, a plastic container 'filled' with butagas, town gas or natural gas. Place the sensor and compensator in the container and cover loosely with a lid. It may take 30 seconds before the circuit responds. It often takes several minutes for the circuit to recover when the gas is removed. *Beware of igniting the gas by sparks or naked flames and do not smoke while testing.*

Components required
Resistors (see p.139)
R1   220Ω
R2,R3   10k (2 off)
R4,R5   gas sensor and compensator (matched pair)
R6   27k
RV1   4k7 miniature horizontal preset potentiometer
RV2   10k miniature horizontal preset potentiometer

Capacitors
C1   100n polyester
C2   1μ electrolytic

Semiconductors
Q1   ZTX300 npn transistor

Integrated circuits
IC1   LM317T adjustable power regulator, 1.5A
IC2   CA3140 CMOS operational amplifier

Miscellaneous
SW1   single-pole single-throw toggle switch
stripboard 12 strips by 24 holes, 11 strips by 17 holes
1mm terminal pins (10 off)
suitable plastic enclosure
8-way d.i.l. socket
solid-state AWD or siren
heat sink for IC1 (e.g. twisted vane type, 17°C/W)

Using the projects in a domestic security system

Although the projects of Chapters 2 to 4 are primarily intended as stand-alone devices, many of them are suitable for incorporating into a unified domestic security system. If you begin by building a few of these simpler devices, you will be able to adapt them later should you decide to install a more comprehensive system.

As parts of the domestic system, the projects will no longer need individual AWDs. The AWD is replaced with a relay. Fig 4.12 shows how to modify the usual configuration of the alarm circuit of the project. The output from an amplifier or logic gate is fed through a resistor to a switching transistor. In the original project this transistor has an AWD and possibly an LED in its collector circuit. The AWD is replaced by the coil of the relay.

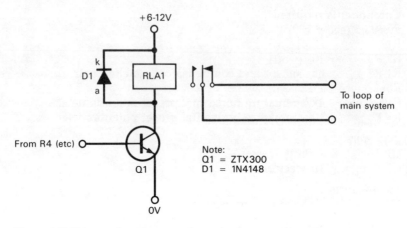

Figure 4.12 Using a relay to connect the project to a security system

Under the alarm condition, the transistor is turned on and current flows through the relay coil. The diode D1 is required to protect the transistor against large voltages generated when the relay is switched off. If you prefer to leave the existing AWD in place, the relay and diode can be connected in parallel with the AWD, so providing both a general and local warning sound.

There is a wide range of small pcb-mounting relays available, sold as 'miniature relays', 'sub-miniature relays' and 'ultra-miniature relays'. The current to be switched is only 1mA so it is well within the ratings of any relay of this type. Choose one that is rated to operate at the voltage used by the project circuit — this need not necessarily be the same voltage as that on which the main domestic system operates.

In most projects there is room for the relay on the main circuit board, perhaps in the place formerly occupied by the AWD. If there is not, mount the relay on a small scrap of board and attach this to the inside of the case using Blu-tack or a double-sided self-adhesive pad.

It gives greater security against deliberate cutting of the wires if the relay is wired into the normally closed loop of the security system (p. 98). For this reason, the chosen relay should have a change-over switch (i.e. a single-pole double-throw switch). The normally closed contact pair is wired into the system. In the alarm condition the relay coil is energised, the switch opens, the loop is broken and the alarm is triggered.

5 A multi-channel system – phase A

The remaining chapters deal with a system that brings together all or almost all the security devices in your home into one integrated system. This may include one or more of the stand-alone devices described in earlier chapters as well as a complete protection for all the doors and windows of the house. With everything connected to one system you have complete control of home security from a centrally located panel. The system is designed to be:

★ flexible – it accepts any combination of security devices, including fire and flood warnings, so it can be tailor-made to your requirements.
★ expandable – you can start with a small easily-installed system and add further features to it as and when you are able.

When fully developed it incorporates all the facilities found in most commercial systems. This chapter describes the minimal system, known as phase A. The expanded systems, phases B and C are described in Chapters 6 and 7 respectively.

One of the essential features of an integrated system such as this is the *loop*. This literally is a loop of wire that runs to various parts of the house linking the security devices and sensors to the central control unit. There may be more than one loop, each concerned with protecting different regions of the house or with different types of protection. For example, there may be separate loops for the ground floor and the first floor, allowing the protection for each floor to be activated independently. There may be a special loop for hazard detecting devices, such as fire sensors, so that these can be left active when the rest of the system is switched off. One of the most important types of loop is a *peripheral loop*.

Peripheral loop

The first line of defence against the intruder is to ensure that there is no way of gaining entry to the house without sounding the alarm. Usually, the only entry points are the external doors and the windows. Each of these is fitted with a switch which is normally closed, arranged so that it is impossible for the door or window to be opened without opening the switch.

The switches are all wired in series in a loop (Fig 5.1). If any door or window is opened, the loop is broken. Breaking of the loop is detected electronically (see later) and the alarm sounds. Should an intruder attempt to cut a hole in the window-glass, reach through, and cut the wire of the loop, this too breaks the loop and the alarm sounds. As an additional precaution, the loop can include metal foil across each window pane.

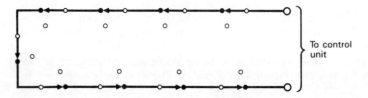

Figure 5.1 Peripheral loop of normally closed switches, wired in series

A peripheral loop takes several hours to install, but little technical skill is required and there is no doubt that it provides a most robust and reliable defence. By 'robust', we mean that the mechanics of it are simple and there is little that can go wrong. By 'reliable' we mean that it will unfailingly detect an entry or an attempt at entry, but is unlikely to trigger a false alarm. The materials required to set up a peripheral loop are inexpensive and, provided you do the work yourself, the loop gives excellent protection for relatively little cost.

Installing a peripheral loop involves running a wire to all windows and doors so, before embarking on the project, you need to consider the visual effects of the wiring on the appearance of the room. You may possibly consider that it may not be desirable to wire up certain windows or doors for this reason. With a carefully planned route, it is usually possible to conceal the greater part of the wiring. It can be tacked to door and window frames so that it is out of sight. If you have floor-length curtains, it can be run down behind these and then along the tops of skirting boards.

Wire can be run under most kinds (but not all kinds — try it out first) of carpet without showing. The wire under carpets may eventually wear through, causing a break in the loop, but this is very unlikely. Runs of wire that are unavoidably visible may be made less conspicuous if light-duty wire with white PVC insulation is used. In any case, light-duty wire is the cheapest for the purpose.

If you are having a room decorated, it is sometimes possible to install the wiring before the room is papered. If, after considering all possibilities, you decide that the wires are sure to ruin the decor of your best room, then you will have to resort to stand-alone devices, such as Projects 2, 11 and 14, for such rooms.

When you are planning the peripheral loop, remember that intruders may be able to gain access to your home by other means than through doors and windows. The enterprising caller may decide to use a skylight or a coal chute, for example. Study your home carefully from inside and out and try to decide how *you* would attempt to get in if you had lost your key and were locked out.

Switches for the peripheral loop
As shown in Fig 5.1, these have 'normally closed' contacts. Below we list the various types of switch suitable for this purpose:

(1) Magnetic switches:
These were described in connection with Project 1. They are the most useful type of switch for the peripheral loop.

(2) Micro-switches:
There are many ways of using these. An example was given in the booby trap (Project 6), but they can also be used for protecting a door or windows, particularly one of unusual construction for which the standard magnetic switches are unsuitable. A booby-trap switch can be included as part of the peripheral loop.

(3) Window foil:
This is self-adhesive aluminium foil which is fixed to the glass of the window. The ends of the foil are clamped in special terminating blocks, which connect the foil into the peripheral loop. If the glass is broken, the foil tears and the loop is broken.

Fig 5.2 shows various ways of fixing the foil. The simplest and most economical, though the most unsightly, is to fix the strip

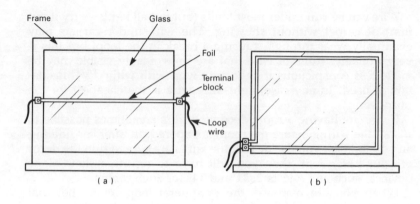

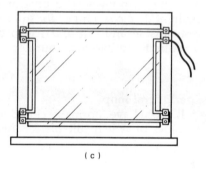

Figure 5.2 Patterns for window foil

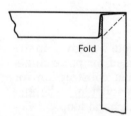

Figure 5.3 Pleating the corners of a window foil pattern, so that there is no electrical discontinuity

straight across the window, as in (a). Fig 5.3(b) shows an effective pattern that does not unduly obstruct the view from the window. The disadvantage of this pattern is that it is possible for the intruder to short-circuit the foil loop by cutting a small hole in the window, connecting a jumper lead across its two ends, and then making a much larger hole. This can be made more difficult if the point of connection to the loop is less obvious as in Fig 5.2(c).

The adhesive on one side of the tape prevents electrical contact if one length of tape is stuck down on another. For this reason the corners in patterns such as (b) and (c) are made by folding the tape as in Fig 61, without tearing it.

(4) Vibration detectors:
These may be attached to doors or windows. Special types are available with an adhesive pad for attaching the sensor to window glass. The contacts of these detectors are normally closed but any vibration, such as that produced by an attempt to smash a door or window, causes the contacts to open.

Another form of vibration detector is the mercury tilt switch. Some of these act as a closed switch when in a certain position and as an open switch when tilted. They could be used for detecting when a ventilator or louvred window is opened. The other type of mercury switch is closed in *any* position and opens whenever it is disturbed. This type functions as a vibration detector or movement detector, and has many applications in booby traps.

Junction boxes for the peripheral loop
Some kinds of switch and the window foil blocks have terminals to which the wires of the loop may be connected. Other kinds of switch have cables which must be taken to a nearby junction box for connection to the loop.

To avoid the possibility of the intruder opening the junction box and short-circuiting the switch, it is preferable to use tamper-proof junction boxes. These have a pair of contacts built in to the cover of the box. The contacts are wired into the loop, acting as switches. If the cover of the box is in place, the contacts are held closed, but if any attempt is made to remove the cover, the contacts part and the loop is broken.

If it is necessary for the loop to be wired to a device on a movable support, such as a door, the connection is made by using two junction boxes connected by a length of flexible, durable cable. Pairs of boxes connected by special cable are available from electronics suppliers.

Overview of the multi-channel system

Phase A, basic system:
This is just a single-channel system, consisting of channel 2, operating with a single loop. The loop may be a peripheral loop as described above, but also include any of the special detectors such

as the ultrasonic intruder detector and smoke alarm, and a few booby-traps. There is provision for expanding the system to control up to six channels at a later date.

The master switch of the control unit is lockable. Only persons in possession of the key are able to arm or disarm the system. The control unit is tamper-proof; any attempt to open the control box sets off the alarm. Although it is mains-powered, the unit houses a back-up battery, making it proof against failure of the mains supply, or disconnection from the supply. It uses the type of siren unit described in Project 13 so that the siren sounds if the wires from the control unit are cut. The control unit has a warning lamp to indicate the alarm condition on each loop. The alarm sounds for a fixed period of 2 to 20 minutes, and then switches off.

One omission from phase A, remedied in phase B, is that you can not include the exit door (see below). Instead, you will have to rely on the physical protection of a mortice dead-lock to protect this door.

Phase B, standard system:
This has all the features of phase A, and provides protection for the exit door. In any house, it is always possible to make doors absolutely secure (except perhaps against an explosive charge) by installing suitably strong bolts or chains on the inside. It is also possible to protect windows with steel grilles or armour-plated glass. But there always has to be a door by which the occupants leave the premises when they are to be left unoccupied. This is the exit door. It can not be bolted or chained from the inside so is physically less secure than the other doors.

It helps if the door is one that is clearly visible to passers-by, for this gives a would-be intruder less time to work on the door unobserved. Even so, the addition of electronic protection to the exit door is a big advantage.

On leaving the house, a built-in delay circuit gives you up to 3 minutes to depart, during which time the exit door may be opened without triggering the alarm. On your return to the house, using the exit door, the alarm does not sound at first. You must go to the control panel and disarm the system, using the key, before 30 seconds have elapsed. The alarm sounds if the system is not disarmed within that time. The chance of an intruder knowing that the system has to be disabled, being able to find the control box within such a short time, and having a key that fits the lock of the master switch is remote.

Phase C, optional extensions:
Phases A or B may be extended by fitting one or more of the following options:

(a) Channels 1 and 4 : Additional channels with the same features as channel 2, operating as normally closed loops. These allow you to define independent security areas. For example, if channel 1 is for the upstair rooms only, it would not normally be used when the house is occupied. Bedroom windows could be

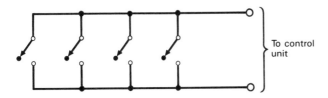

Figure 5.4 Loop of normally open switches, wired in parallel

opened at night. You could wire the special intruder detectors of Chapters 2 and 3 on channel 4. With this channel switched off, the house has perimeter security but the occupants can safely move from room to room without setting off proximity detectors or booby-traps.

(b) Channel 5: This is for devices such as pressure mats that have normally open switches. You may also have commercially built sensors that switch in this mode. Normally open switches are wired in parallel (Fig 5.4). Closing any one switch completes the circuit through the loop and triggers the alarm. If any part of the main loop is cut, the part beyond the loop becomes ineffective. It is therefore important that the wiring of this loop should be well concealed.

(c) Channel 6: This loop is intended for fire-detectors, flood-detectors, panic buttons and other devices that should be ready for action 24 hours a day. The loop is active whether or not the other channels are armed or disarmed. It is not inactivated while you are leaving or entering the house by the exit door. The only way this loop can be switched off is by opening the control unit and cutting off the power supply. These precautions make it almost impossible for these essential safety devices to be left in an inactive state by accident. The loop operates with normally closed switches so any fault in the loop wiring is immediately apparent.

(d) Delays on channels 4 and 5: The delay on channel 3 when

leaving and entering the house can be extended to any of the other channels

(e) Second siren: There is the option of associating channel 6 with a second siren, which emits a sound different from the main one. Occupants of the house will know whether the alarm is due to intruders or to a hazard, such as fire. There is provision for channel 6 to be set to trigger either the main siren or the second siren or both sirens. There is no timed cut-out on the second siren.

(f) Switch-tampering detector: This sounds the alarm if anyone changes the setting of any of the channel-selecting switches on the control unit. The setting may be altered only when the system is disarmed, by using the key.

Project 18 The phase A system

How it works
The circuit for sensing the state of a normally closed loop is shown in Fig 5.5. This is used with channels 1 to 4. As long as the loop is complete, the voltage at terminal A is pulled down to 0V. If the loop is broken, by opening a door or smashing a window, for example, the voltage rises immediately to 12V. This is a logic-high output, which is fed to IC1 in the main circuit. The high level also makes base current flow to the transistor, which is turned on. Its

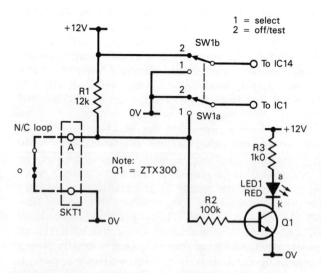

Figure 5.5 Input sub-circuit for normally closed loops

collector current illuminates LED1, indicating the 'alarm' condition.

There is a double-pole double throw (DPDT) switch which, in position 1, feeds the logic high to IC1 of the main control circuit. In position 2 this switch is connected to 0V (logic low), inactivating the loop, but allowing the LED indicator to be used for testing the devices connected to this loop.

The second pole of the switch (the top one in the drawing) is part of the switch tampering detector circuit, phase C, option (f). This second pole is not required at phases A and B. A single-pole switch could be used, but it is better to install a DPDT switch now, so that the option may be added later.

Fig 5.6 shows the main control circuit, configured for phase B and all the options of phase C. As will be explained in the construction notes, the wiring for phase A is simpler in places. The signals from all channels and the other detector circuits are fed to IC1, an 8-input NOR gate. All inputs to this gate are normally logic low and the output is normally high.

In phase A, only the 'tamper' and channel 2 inputs are used, the inputs for unused channels being wired to 0V. The output of IC1 goes low if any one (or possibly more) of the gate inputs goes high. While the output is high, the capacitor C1 is charged to +12V. However, when the output goes low the charge falls to 0V. The rise and fall times are about half a second. This means that short-lived changes in the output of the gate do not affect subsequent stages in the system.

The importance of this is the avoidance of false alarms. Loops of wire running around the rooms of a house act like radio antennae, picking up all kinds of electrical disturbance. When a room light is turned on, or the refrigerator motor switches off, the electromagnetic radiation produced by the sparking switch contacts generates electrical pulses in the security loops. These brief spikes, the equivalent of logic highs or lows, are readily detected by logic gates. They can easily trigger a false alarm. The combination of R4 and C1 damps out these spurious pulses and makes the system free from such interference.

The next step in control is the arming switch SW2. This is lockable for maximum security. As an alternative to a mechanical lock, use a key-pad that responds to the entry of a personal indentification number (PIN). The author's *Digital Electronics Projects for Beginners*, also published by PC Publishing, describes a combination door sentry. A simple modifcation of the circuit, given later, enables this project to be used for this purpose.

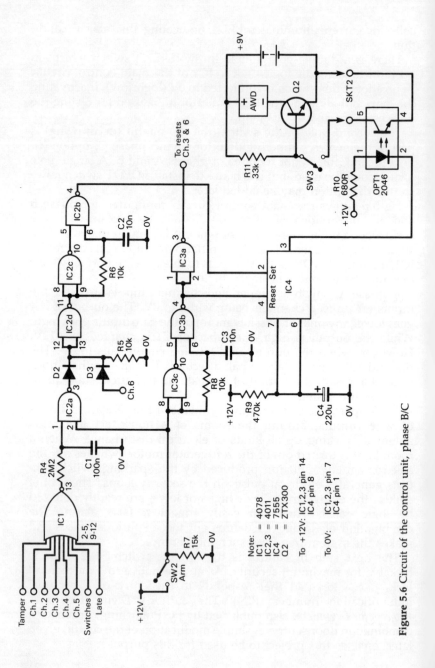

Figure 5.6 Circuit of the control unit, phase B/C

When SW2 is open, IC2, pin 2 is low and the output of the NAND gate remains high at all times. When the switch is closed, pin 2 is high and the signal from IC1 can now pass through the gate. The output of the gate is normally low but goes high in the 'alarm' condition. The next step (only applicable to phase C) allows channel 6 to trigger the alarm. This is done with a Mickey-Mouse OR gate consisting of D2, D3 and R5.

In phase A this gate is not necessary; a simple wire link runs from pin 3 to pins 12 and 13 of IC2. The next two gates are wired to make a pulse generator. In the 'alarm' condition pin 11 of IC2 goes low and triggers the generator. A short low pulse goes to the SET terminal of the timer. The output of the timer goes high, turning on the alarm, which is a solid-state audible warning device (AWD). The AWD sounds for a period, the length of which is determined by the values of R9 and C4. With the values shown in Fig 5.6, the AWD sounds for approximately two minutes. For a longer period, use a resistor of higher value. For example, 4M7 gives 20 minutes.

The gates of IC3 are wired as a second pulse generator to reset the timer when the arming switch is opened. This silences the system. The output from the generator is inverted by a NAND gate for use in resetting channels 3 and 6. It is convenient to wire up this gate at phase A, but its output is not used.

The AWD has the same sub-circuit as in Project 13. To hold the alarm off, the wires joining the alarm to the control unit must be intact and the phototransistor in the optocoupler OPT1 must be conducting. The normally low output of the timer ensures that current is flowing through the LED of OPT1 so the phototransistor is conducting. When the output goes high the LED is turned off, the phototransistor ceases to conduct and the AWD is activated.

Fig 5.7 shows the circuit for the control unit tamper-proof

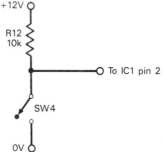

Figure 5.7 Circuit for the tamper switch

switch, SW4. This is a microswitch positioned so that its actuator is slightly depressed by the lid of the box when it is fastened in position. The switch contacts are closed. As soon as the lid is loosened, the switch opens and the input to IC1 goes high, triggering the alarm. A mercury tilt switch could be fitted as an alternative to a microswitch.

Power supply
Phase A requires approximately 20mA, so it would be feasible to operate it on a battery only, especially if the system is to be used only at nights. However, if the system is to operate for 24 hours a day to provide fire warnings, and to operate without attention for two weeks or more while you are away on holiday, it is preferable to use mains power. An inexpensive mains power supply unit ('battery eliminator') giving an unregulated supply up to 300mA

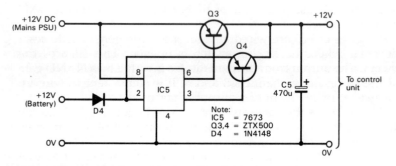

Figure 5.8 Battery back-up circuit

at 12V DC is all that is needed. This plugs into a mains socket, the body of the plug containing the power supply circuit, with a light-duty lead that runs to the control unit. To guard against mains power failure, there is a back-up battery and a circuit (Fig 5.8) which detects failure of the mains supply and automatically switches on the battery.

Constructing phase A
Unless you have definitely decided to restrict your system to phase A, it is best to start with a board big enough to hold phase B and all the options of phase C. The stripboard diagrams in this chapter and Chapters 6 and 7 all assume such a board, 34 strips wide and 73 holes long.

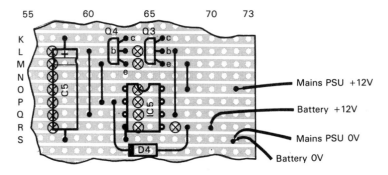

Figure 5.9 Battery back-up circuit, located to right of IC6. If located to the right of OPT1, the strips are those lettered T to BB

As the stripboard diagram (Fig 5.9) shows, the battery back-up circuit is located to the right of IC6, when this is installed in phase B. Power line wires are soldered from K57 to T57 (+12V) and from S56 to BB56 (0V) to connect the circuit to the phase A ics on the lower third of the board (Fig 5.10) and to the input channels. However, if you are building a phase A system only and using a narrower board (15 strips wide), it can be located in the blank area to the right of OPT1. In this case the power rails of the back-up circuit are T and BB, so they are continuous with those supplying the ics.

The battery back-up ic (IC5) requires that the battery voltage is lower than the voltage from the mains unit. The silicon diode D4 in series with the battery, drops the voltage by about 0.6V to ensure this. Provided that you do not experience unduly prolonged or frequent cuts in mains power, a small battery of 8 size AA alkaline cells in a battery box will suffice. Such a battery has a capacity of about 2Ah, so will provide power to run a phase A system for about 100 hours, or a phase B or C system for about 50 hours.

Begin with the construction of the battery back-up sub-circuit. When it is complete, connect the mains power supply and the 12V battery supply. The voltage across C5 is close to 12V. When the mains is switched off, the voltage drops slightly to about 11V. Disconnect the battery, which is not required further during construction.

Mount the ics and their associated components (except switches) in order from IC1 to IC4, followed by OPT1. The unused inputs of

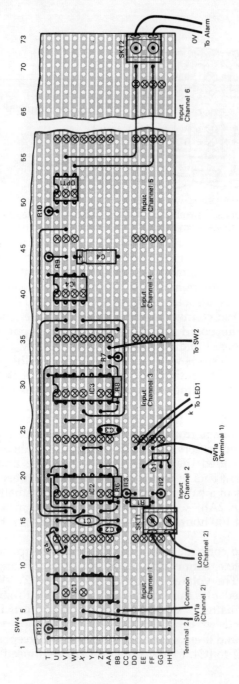

Figure 5.10 Stripboard layout of the control unit, phase A

IC1 (pins 3, 5 and 9 to 12) are wired to 0V for this phase. D2, D3 and R5 are omitted, there being a plain wire link from W16 to V21 instead.

Test the circuit at these stages:

IC1 — Temporarily wire the pin at V4 to the 0V rail; wire X5 to FF24; insert a short loop of wire in SKT1, with one end loosely gripped so that it can be pulled out and re-inserted easily to open and close the 'loop'. Temporarily mount LED1 in holes DD22 (anode) and EE22 (cathode). IC1 pin 13 is high and the LED is off when the loop is closed. Pin 13 is low and the LED is on when the loop is opened.

IC2 and IC3 — temporarily connect the pin at AA34 to the +12V rail (system armed). IC2 pin 1 falls to low when the loop is opened, taking about 0.5s (but the exact time does not matter). The output at IC2 pin 3 goes high, and at pin 11 goes low. With AA34 connected to 0V, pin 3 remains low and pin 11 remains high, whatever the state of the loop. IC2 pin 4 and IC3 pin 4 remain high; it is not easy to detect the short low pulses but their action can be confirmed later, when testing IC4.

IC4 — decide on the length of time for which the siren is to sound and use an appropriate value for R9. It makes testing much quicker if a resistor of lower value is temporarily wired in parallel with R9 (at T45/V45), to reduce the 'on' time. A 47k resistor, for example, gives an 'on' period of just over 10s. If AA34 is connected to +12V to arm the system, the output at pin 3 is normally low but goes high when the loop is opened. This confirms that the pulse generator of IC2 is working properly. If AA34 is connected to 0V during an 'on' period, pin 3 immediately goes low. This confirms that the pulse generator of IC3 is working.

OPT1 — before testing this, build the alarm circuit board see Project 13, (Fig 3.23). SW1 is the tamper switch of the alarm cover, if fitted referred to as SW3 in Fig 5.6. If the wires at G9 and H1 are left unconnected, the AWD sounds as soon as the 9V battery is connected. Twisting the bare ends of the two loose wires together silences the AWD. If the sound is weak, replace R11 (= R1 in Fig 3.23) with a resistor of lower value. Now insert the loose wires into SKT1, making sure that the 0V wire (from H1) goes to the terminal at FF72. Provided that the control board has its power supply on, the AWD is silent.

With the system armed, opening the loop makes the LED come on; the AWD sounds for just over 10s. You will find that you can open the loop very briefly and then close it again without triggering the AWD; this shows that the system is almost certainly

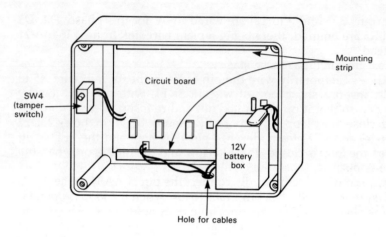

Figure 5.11 Arrangement of circuit inside control box

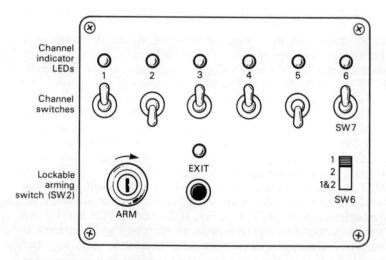

Figure 5.12 Control box panel

proof against false alarms. With the system disarmed (AA34 to 0V) the AWD is silent, whatever the state of the loop. If either of the wires are removed from SKT2, the AWD sounds indefinitely.

Remove the temporary connections, the LED and the resistor at T45/V45. The board is now ready to be installed. The board is best mounted at the back of the control box, using self-adhesive mounting strip that grips its edges (Fig 5.11). The lead from the mains PSU enters through a hole at the rear. The same hole is used for the wires going to the main loop and the siren. The back-up battery is fixed in front of the circuit-board, using a lump of Blu-tack or a two-sided self-adhesive pad (a 'Sticky-Fixer'). The switches and LEDs are mounted on the front panel, normally the lid of the box. Fig 5.12 shows the panel layout for the full 6-channel system. At phase A the channel switch and indicator LED are located in the positions allocated to channel 2. A microswitch (the tamper switch SW4) is glued to one side of the box, so that its actuator is held depressed (contacts closed) when the lid of the box is in place.

Installing the system

First decide on the approximate layout of the loop, what rooms it will go to and and what devices are to be included in it. These include the control panel itself. Here are some points to consider:

★ It must be reasonably near to a mains socket.

★ If you are installing a peripheral loop, it must not be possible for anyone to reach the control box without passing through the loop, i.e. not within physical reach of an open or smashed window.

★ Preferably it should be out of sight of persons outside the house — an upstairs location is best.

★ It should be hard to find. Hide it in a cupboard (e.g. the airing cupboard), but make sure that the power wires and other wires do not give the game away. The airing cupboard is quite a good place as there are often pipes running up to the loft and this makes it easier to run wires up to the loft for the siren. Also it is relatively inexpensive to have a mains socket installed in the airing cupboard if the wiring for an immersion heater is already there. Or hide it in a desk or bureau.

★ It must be possible for you to get to the control box and disarm the system without triggering the alarm. For example, do not place it at the far end of a corridor protected by an ultrasonic beam.

★ Thinking ahead to phase B, you must be able to get from the exit door to the control box within 30 seconds, even when the house is in darkness due to a power cut.

Decide on the location of the siren. Here are some points to think about:

★ It should not be readily accessible. Otherwise an intruder can silence the system quickly by smashing the siren before entering the house. Place it in as high and remote a location as possible. An ideal place is the loft or on the outside of the house above second-storey level. Check that all long ladders are always locked away.

★ It must be clearly audible to neighbours. The outside of the building is best.

★ If outside, it must be weatherproof. Some types of siren are already weatherproofed. Others may be housed in a steel enclosure mounted on the side of the house. The better models of enclosure have tamper-proof contacts (SW3, Fig 5.6) which open when someone begins to loosen the cover, long before it is possible to remove it completely.

★ If it is not practicable to mount the siren outdoors, mount it indoors where it is not likely to be seen by an intruder. Possibly mount two sirens in different hidden places, wiring them in parallel.

★ Dummy siren enclosures, mounted on the side of the house with no siren inside are a decoy and a deterrent.

As mentioned above, wires can often be run up to the loft alongside hot water pipes. A builder will be able to drill a hole through brickwork in the loft for running the wires to an outdoor siren.

Having decided on the locations of the control box and siren, it only remains to plan the course of the wiring. It is best to plan everything in detail *before* beginning the wiring, as it is fairly easy to take the wrong route by mistake and then have to remove the wiring, wasting time and leaving unsightly holes in the woodwork and plaster.

Key-panel arming
As an alternative to the lockable arming switch, there are a number of key-panels available ready-made with relay contacts that can be wired in place of SW2. A 4-digit code number is entered to arm or disarm the system. With some of these, the combination can be changed frequently. The exact details depend on the specification of the key-panel used, so the manufacturer's instructions must be consulted before deciding if any given key-panel is suited for this purpose and how it may be employed.

A similar device is the Door Sentry described in *Digital Electronics Projects for Beginners* (PC Publishing). The circuit of the sentry is best housed in the same case as the control unit, with the keys and display mounted on the panel. It may be powered from the 12V supply, provided that R7 to R13 are replaced by resistors of 1

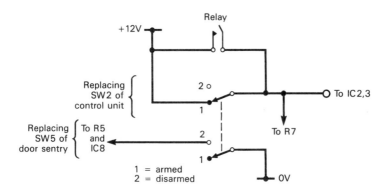

Figure 5.13 Using the door sentry (see text) as a disarming key-pad

kilohm. The AWD is replaced by a miniature relay with a 12V coil, and normally open contacts (or changeover contacts with wiring to the normally open pair). The reset button of the sentry is hidden away at some distance from the panel, using concealed wiring as much as possible. The lockable arming switch (SW2) of the control unit and the OPEN switch (SW5) of the sentry are replaced by a double-pole double-throw switch, wired in parallel with the relay contacts, as in Fig 5.13.

Starting with the system disarmed, press the reset button, then press key 'C' to clear the counters of the sentry. Key 'P' may be pressed a few times to display a digit other than '0' if preferred. The system is armed by operating the arming switch. This can be done by anybody and does not now require the use of a key. However before the switch can be set to disarm the system, the correct 4-digit code must be keyed in. If any mistake is made, the relay contacts close, short-circuiting the arming switch, so the system stays permanently armed, even if the switch is set to disarm it. It may only be disarmed then by pressing the hidden reset button. For greater security, this could be a lockable switch.

Components required
Resistors (see p.139)
R1	12k
R2	100k
R3	1k
R4	2M2
R6,R8,R12	10k (3 off)

R7	15k
R9	470k (see text)
R10	680Ω
R11	33k

Capacitors

C1	100n polyester
C2,C3	10n polyester (2 off)
C4	220µ electrolytic
C5	470µ electrolytic

Semiconductors

D1	LED red
D4	1N4148 silicon signal diode
Q1,Q2	ZTX300 npn transistor (2 off)
Q3,Q4	ZTX500 pnp transmitter (2 off)
OPT1	2046 optocoupler

Integrated circuits

IC1	4078B CMOS 8-input NOR gate
IC2,IC3	4011B CMOS quadruple 2-input NAND gate (2 off)
IC4	7555 CMOS timer
IC5	7673 battery back-up ic

Miscellaneous

SW1	double-pole double-throw toggle switch
SW2	lockable panel-mounting single-pole single-throw switch
SW4	miniature micro-switch
SKT1, SKT2	2-way pcb socket (2 off)
9V	AA battery box (for siren)
12V	AA battery box (battery back-up)

battery clip (2 off)
AA alkaline cells (12 off)
audible warning device, 6-12V low-current (20mA) solid state siren, or similar
enclosure for AWD (if required for outdoors mounting)
mains adaptor PSU 12V dc unregulated, at 300mA
stripboard 34 strips by 73 holes, and 6 strips by 9 holes
1mm terminal pins (15 off)
suitable plastic enclosure
8-way d.i.l. sockets (3 off)
14-way d.i.l. sockets (3 off)
materials for peripheral loop (reel 10/0.1 single cable, white PVC; magnetic switches; window foil and terminals)

6 A multi-channel system – phase B

This chapter deals with an extension to the system described in Chapter 5. This increases the security and convenience of the system by including the exit door.

Project 19 The phase B system

How it works

The exit door has a magnetic switch wired into a loop connected to the channel 3 input circuit. The circuit is the same as that used for channel 2 (Fig 5.5). In the delay circuit (Fig 6.1) the gates are numbered to make the description easier to follow. The circuit relies on two flip-flops (G1/G2, G3/G4) to act as memories. When the control unit is armed by closing SW1 (Fig 6.1) a pulse to G2 and G4 resets the flip-flops. Pin 10 and pin 4 are high; pin 11 and pin 3 are low. The timer T1 has a low output, so the output of G8 is high and its inputs to G9, G10 and G11 are high. G9 to G12 are AND gates, so already having one input high, their output takes the same state as the other input. A high input on channel 3, caused by opening the exit door, passes through G15 and G9 to IC1 and the alarm is triggered.

So far we have seen the circuit operating in exactly the same way as channel 2, to sound the alarm when the door is opened. The delay function of this circuit is used when you wish to leave the house unoccupied. When you are ready to leave, arm the system and press the EXIT button (SW5). This sets the flip-flop G1/G2 (the 'going' flip-flop). Pin 10 goes low, triggering the pulse generator G6/G7 to produce a low pulse which triggers T1. Its output goes high, LED5 comes on, and the output of G8 goes low. With one

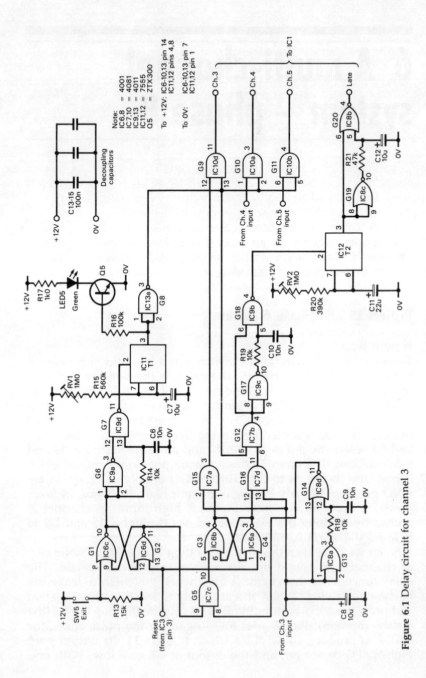

Figure 6.1 Delay circuit for channel 3

input to each of the AND gates G9-G11 low, their output is low whatever the state of the other input. The exit door may now be opened without sending a triggering pulse to IC1. RV1 is set to give a period between 1 and 3 minutes. After that period, the output of T1 falls again and any attempt to open the door sounds the alarm.

If you leave the house within the timed period, the sequence of events is as follows. Opening the door has no effect but closing the door produces a high pulse from G13/G14. Now that G1/G2 is set (= 'going') this pulse passes through G5 and sets G3/G4 (= 'gone'). It is essential not to open the door again after this, even though the original timing period is still running. The door must be opened and closed once only. Opening the door a second time counts as 'coming back home again', as explained below. This is the reason for the capacitor C8 on the channel 3 input line. The door switch might make and break contacts several times in a fraction of a second as it is opened and closed. These makes and breaks would count as opening and closing the door more than once. C8 debounces the door switch to prevent this.

The next time the door is opened (i.e. when you return to the house after your expedition), G3/G4 is already set (pin 3 high), so G16 goes high. As the original 'going' timing period is now over, G8 is high, so G12 goes high and this triggers G17/G18 to trigger the timer T2. Its output goes high. You now have a period of 10 to 30 seconds to disarm the system. If you do not do this in time, the output of T2 goes low, triggering G9/G10. This produces a fairly long high pulse which goes to IC1 and sounds the alarm.

Constructing phase B

It is assumed that you have already constructed and tested Phase A, complete with its siren and power supply.

First assemble input channel 3, which has the same layout as channel 2 (Fig 5.10). Connect the channel switch SW1a as follows: terminal 1 to the pin at EE34; terminal 2 to the pin at L25; common to the pin at S25. For testing, temporarily solder in an LED, and connect a short length of wire between the terminals of the socket to act as the loop to the exit door. There are so many interconnections between ics in this project that the only course is to complete the whole circuit before testing it. Fig 6.1 shows three connections between IC10 and IC1, but only that from IC10 pin 11 to IC1 pin 5 is made at this stage. Remember to cut the strip beneath IC1 at Y7.

A connection is also required from IC8 pin 4 to IC1 pin 12.

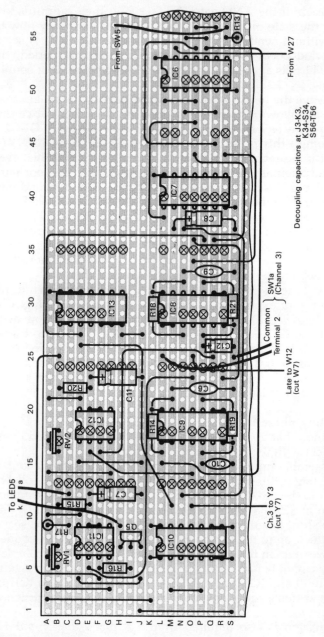

Figure 6.2 Stripboard layout of delay circuit for channel 3

Remember to cut W7. Connect IC3 pin 3 (W27) to IC6 pin 13. Before testing the circuit, it is essential to solder the three decoupling capacitors in place. These are intended to damp out transient spikes on the supply lines which may affect the operation of the ics. If you experience trouble, particularly flip-flops changing state when they should not, or failing to change when they should, try adding one or two more decoupling capacitors. Solder them across the 0V and +12V rails, positioning them between the existing decoupling capacitors.

The completed circuit is tested by putting it through its normal cycle of action. For this purpose it is best if the alarm is *not* connected. Instead, monitor pin 3 of IC4, using a testmeter or logic probe. This goes high in the alarm condition.

First test the normal action of the loop *without* the delay:

(1) Switch on power and close SW2. This resets the flip-flops; on IC6, pins 4 and 10 are high, pins 3 and 10 are low. If this fails, check the pulse-generator (IC3) and the flip-flop wiring.

(2) Opening the loop for channel 2 gives the alarm condition.

(3) Close loop 2: repeat step 1: opening the loop for channel 3 gives the alarm condition. The outputs from flip-flops are as above. If this fails, check the channel 3 input, the action of G15 and G9, and the connection to IC1.

Now test the delay circuit. If there is failure at any stage, make the checks suggested. Then repeat the sequence *from the beginning*:

(4) As step 1 above.

(5) Press SW5 (EXIT). IC6 pin 10 goes low; pin 11 goes high. LED5 comes on. IC10 pins 2, 5 and 13 go low. If this fails check G6, G7, IC11 and G8.

(6) Open channel 3 loop; no change of flip-flops; provided LED5 is still lit, G16 and G12 stay low. If LED5 is not lit, return to step 4 and repeat.

(7) Close channel 3 loop; IC6 pin 3 goes high; pin 4 goes low. If this fails, check the wiring of G3/G4 and the action of G5; pin 9 should be high and pin 8 low, but goes high when the loop is broken.

(8) Wait until LED5 goes out. Then opening the loop of channel 5 triggers T2; its output goes high. If this fails, check G16, G12, G17, G18 and T2.

(9) After 10-30 seconds the output of T2 falls and we have the alarm condition. If this fails, check G19, G20 and the connection to IC1.

(10) Repeat steps 4 to 8 above, then immediately disarm the

system by opening SW1. There is no alarm condition and the outputs of the flip-flops return to those at step 1.

The board is now ready for re-installing in the box. Before doing this you may wish to adjust RV1 and RV2 to obtain suitable timing periods. Mount S5, and D5 as shown in Fig 5.12.

Components required
(R1, R2, R3, Q1, D1 and S1 are for the input sub-circuit)

Resistors (see p.139)

R1	12k
R2,R16	100k (2 off)
R3,R17	1k (2 off)
R13	15k
R14,R18,R19	10k (3 off)
R15	560k
R20	390k
R21	47k
RV1,RV2	vertical sub-miniature preset resistors 1M (2 off)

Capacitors

C6,C9,C10	10n polyester (3 off)
C7	100μ electrolytic
C8,C12	10μ electrolytic (2 off)
C11	22μ electrolytic
C13-C15	100n polyester or ceramic disc (3 off)

Semiconductors

LED1	LED red
LED5	LED green
Q1,Q5	ZTX300 npn transistor (2 off)

Integrated circuits

IC6,IC8	4001B CMOS quadruple 2-input NOR gate (2 off)
IC7,IC10	4081B CMOS quadruple 2-input AND gate (2 off)
IC9,IC13	4011B CMOS quadruple 2-input NAND gate (2 off)
IC11,IC12	7555 CMOS timer (2 off)

Miscellaneous

SW1	double-pole double-throw toggle switch
SW5	push-to-make push-button

1mm terminal pins (6 off)
8-way d.i.l. sockets (2 off)
14-way d.i.l. sockets (6 off)
SKT1 2-way pcb socket

7 A multi-channel system – phase C

In this chapter we describe a number of optional extensions to the phase A or phase B systems. There is no need to add channel 3 (Project 9, Chapter 6) to the system before embarking on the somewhat simpler projects of this chapter.

Project 20 Adding channel 1

This operates with a normally closed loop and requires only an additional input circuit (Fig 5.5). The input circuit is located in the area to the bottom left of the board (Fig 5.10) and has exactly the same arrangement as that for channel 2. The output from the circuit runs to IC1 pin 3. Remove the wire from W4 to BB4 and solder terminal pins at W4 and BB7. Connect the channel switch SW1 to these pins and the new pin at FF12. If you have already installed channel 3, you will have cut the strip at W7. If you have not installed channel 3, the strip can be left uncut.

With an additional channel available there is scope for dividing your home into two zones which can be activated independently. Often it is convenient to wire the upstairs and downstairs rooms in separate loops. Or you may use one channel for the the peripheral loop (the first line of defence) and one for the special sensors (second line of defence).

Components required
Resistors (see p. 139)
R1	12k
R2	100k
R3	1k

Semiconductors
LED1   LED red
Q1   ZTX300 npn transistor

Miscellaneous
SW1   double-pole double-throw toggle switch
1mm terminal pins (5 off)
SKT1 2-way pcb socket

Project 21 Adding channel 4

This is another normally closed loop. The procedure is the same
as for Project 20 and the components required are the same. The
input circuit connects to pin 9 of IC1. Melt the solder joining pins
9 and 10 of the ic socket (Y9 and Z9) and remove the solder bridge.
A cold steel blade held against the board between the tracks and
pushed through the molten solder usually separates it cleanly.
Solder terminal pins at Z12 and BB9. Connect the channel switch
SW1 to these pins and the new pin at FF45.

With three normally closed channels at your disposal, you have
scope for a very flexible zoning system.

Project 22 Adding channel 5

This is a loop for devices with normally open switches. These
include pressure mats, commercially made devices that have only
normally open contacts, and devices of your own making in which
normally open contacts are more convenient to use. Pressure mats
are placed under carpets in strategic situations, where they are
nailed or taped to the floor (Fig 2.10). See Project 3 for further
details.

The input circuit differs slightly from that of the other channels
(Fig 7.1), but is built from the same components (see list for Project
20). The stripboard layout is shown in Fig 7.2. Channel 5 is
connected to pin 10 of IC1. Melt the solder joining pins 10 and 11
of the ic socket (X9, Y9) and remove the solder bridges. A cold steel
blade held against the board between the tracks and pushed
through the molten solder usually separates it cleanly.

If you have already installed channel 4, you will have already
broken the solder link between Y9 and Z9. If you have not installed
channel 4, this link can be left. Solder terminal pins at Y10 and

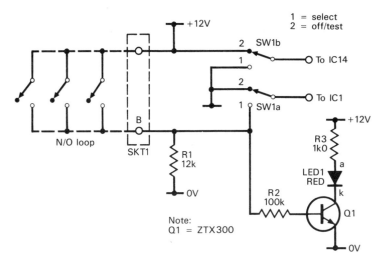

Figure 7.1 Input sub-circuit for normally open loops

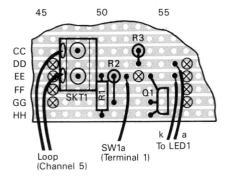

Figure 7.2 Stripboard layout of channel 5

BB12. Connect the channel switch SW1 to these pins and the new pin at FF57. If you have already installed channel 3, you will have cut the strip at Y7. If you have not installed channel 3, the strip can be left uncut.

Project 23 Adding channel 6

Channel 6 is illustrated in Fig 7.3. This has a normally closed loop but the input circuit differs from that of channels 1–4. When the

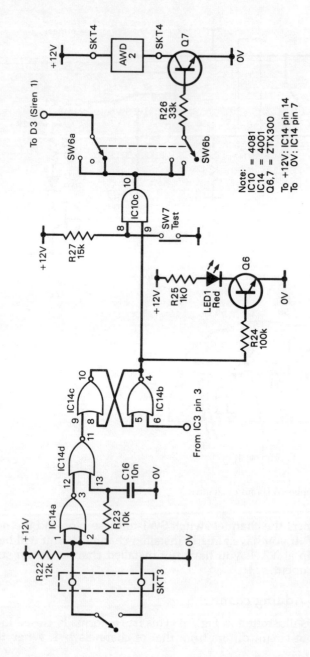

Figure 7.3 circuit for channel 6

system is armed, a pulse from IC3 resets the flip-flop of IC14. As soon as the loop is broken a pulse is generated by the other two gates of IC14, to set the flip-flop. Pin 4 goes high, turning on the warning LED1. The high level passes through the AND gate of IC10 and goes to SW6.

Depending on the setting of SW6, the high level triggers either the main siren (siren 1) or the second siren (siren 2) or both sirens. Siren 1 is triggered when the high level passes through the OR gate formed by the diodes D2 and D3 (Fig 5.6), and on through IC2 to IC4. Routing the signal this way means that the siren sounds whether or not the system is armed, since the NAND gate controlled by the arming switch has been by-passed.

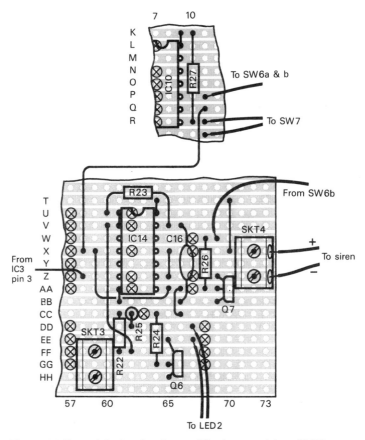

Figure 7.4 Channel 6; also showing modifications to wiring of IC10

This loop is thus suitable for sensors such as fire sensors that need to be kept in action all the time, not just when precautions are being taken against intruders. Once the alarm has been triggered it sounds until the turn-off time has elapsed or the system is disarmed. Siren 2 sounds indefinitely until the system is disarmed.

The operation of channel 6 may be tested by pressing and holding down SW7. If any device on the loop is triggered, the LED comes on but the alarm does not sound. A push-button is used for SW7 and not a switch, so that there is no possibility of the channel accidentally being left in the test mode.

The wiring for the input and logic circuits of channel 6 is shown in Fig 7.4. This shows the modifications to the wiring of IC10. If you have not already mounted IC10 in connection with Project 20, mount it now. Since there are three gates unused at present, their inputs must be connected either to 0V or 12V. Solder pins 1 and 2 together. Solder pins 5, 6 and 7 together and to 0V at S6. Solder pins 12, 13 and 14 together and to + 12V at K9. It is also necessary to wire in the two diodes and the resistor around IC2, to make the OR gate, as shown in Fig 7.5.

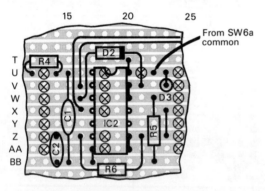

Figure 7.5 Modifying the wiring of IC2 for connecting channel 6

SW6 is a 3-position slide switch for selecting which sirens are to be activated by this system. If channel 6 consists of a number of panic buttons for use by an invalid, for example, you will not want this channel to sound the main siren. Siren 2 could be one or more low-volume solid-state buzzers wired in parallel and located in the downstairs hall and upstairs landing, for example. This switch is optional, and can be omitted. in this event wire the output of IC10 directly to D3 or to R26 or to both.

Components required
Resistors (see p.139)
R5, R23   10k (2 off)
R22   12k
R24   100k
R25   1k
R26   33k
R27   15k

Capacitors
C16   10n polyester

Semiconductors
D2,D3   1N4148 silicon signal diode
LED1   LED red
Q6, Q7   ZTX300 npn transistor (2 off)

Integrated circuits
IC14   4001B CMOS quadruple 2-input NOR gate

Miscellaneous
SW6   Double-pole 3-throw slide switch
SW7   Push-to-make push-button
1mm terminal pins (6 off)
14-way d.i.l. socket
SKT3, SKT 4 2-way pcb socket (2 off)

Project 24 Delays on other channels

It may be convenient to extend the exit door delay of channel 3 to any two other channels. For example, if you have many pressure-mats, this might make it difficult to enter or leave the house without, sooner or later, stepping on one of these and sounding the alarm. The same applies to sensors such as the infra-red or ultrasonic sensors. All that has to be done is to take the connection from the input sub-circuit (i.e. from SW1a common) to one of the gates of IC10 (pin 1 or pin 6) instead of directly to IC1. The gate outputs (pin 3 or pin 4) are connected to the appropriate pin of IC1. Note that this can not be done for any channel that includes a sensor with a latching action. On triggering such a sensor, the loop would be permanently broken and the alarm would sound as soon as the exit period had elapsed. Although it is electronically possible to introduce a delay on channel 6, the special function allocated to this channel precludes this.

Project 25 Switch tampering detector

This circuit sounds the alarm if any of the switches for channels 1 to 4 are altered while the system is armed. Each of the switches SW1 in the input circuits is a double-pole switch (Figs 5.5 and 7.6). Pole 'b' is switched either to 0V (low) or +12V (high), depending on whether the channel is activated or not. Fig 7.6 shows that the logic level of each switch goes *directly* to an exclusive-OR gate and also *indirectly* to the other input of the same gate. The indirect path is through a latch.

When the system is disarmed, with SW2 open, the switches may be altered to select which loops are to be activated. Then SW2 is closed to arm the system. When SW2 is closed, the clock input of IC15 rises from low to high. This causes the data to be latched; in other words, the output Q of each latch takes on the level as input D has at that moment. Since each Q is the same as each D, each exclusive-OR gate receives either two low inputs or two high inputs. The outputs of each gate are low, making pin 1 of IC17 go high and pin 13 go low. This low level is fed to IC1 and has no further effect.

From now on, if any of the switches is altered, D changes but Q does not. The corresponding exclusive-OR gate then receives two *different* inputs and its output goes high. When any one output from IC16 goes high, pin 1 of IC17 goes low and pin 13 goes high. The input to IC 1 goes high and the alarm is triggered.

The layout for this project is shown in Fig 7.7. Wire up the complete circuit, including another 100n decoupling capacitor, soldered to A68 and J68. The wire from D67 goes to IC1 at X11; first remove the wire that runs from X11 to BB11. If you have not already installed channels 4 and 5, there is no need to remove the solder blob connecting pins 9 10 and 11. Test the circuit to confirm that it behaves as described above.

Components required
Capacitors
C17   100n polyester or ceramic disc

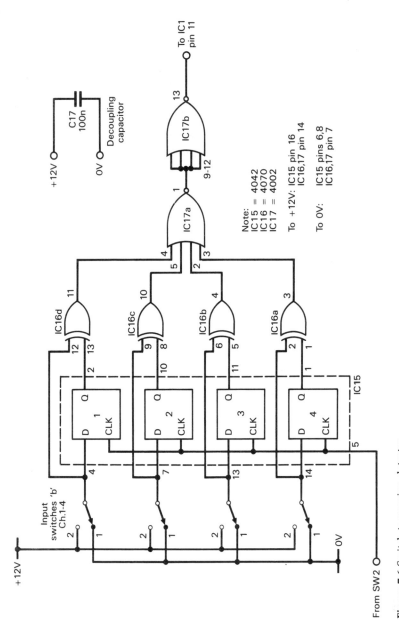

Figure 7.6 Switch tampering detector

131

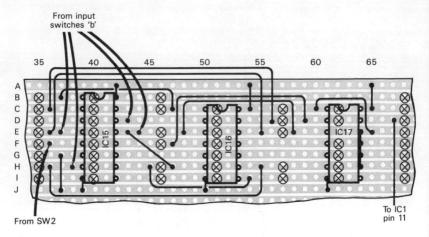

Figure 7.7 Stripboard layout of switch tampering detector

Integrated circuits

IC15	4042B CMOS quadruple latch
IC16	4070B CMOS quadruple exclusive-OR gate
IC17	4002B CMOS dual 4-input NOR gate

Miscellaneous
1mm terminal pins (5 off)
14-way d.i.l. sockets (2 off)
16-way d.i.l. socket

Appendix

Notes for beginners

Stripboard
This is the circuit-building technique used in this book. Stripboard consists of an insulating perforated board with copper strips on one side. There are numerous variants in the arrangement of the strips, but we use the simplest type, which has continuous parallel strips running the length of the board. The strips are perforated with 1mm diameter holes, on a 2.5mm matrix.

Boards are available in a range of sizes. For these projects we have nearly always specified boards in one of the standard sizes. Hovever, it is often more economical to buy one of the largest size boards and cut it into smaller pieces. Terminal pins are available to fit the holes. The pins may be single-sided or double-sided; we use single-sided pins in these projects.

Using stripboard
If you are not using a ready-cut board of standard size, cut the board from a larger one, with a junior hacksaw. A fine flat file or glass-paper block is used to smooth the cut edges.

In most projects some of the strips have to be cut, to separate parts of a strip that are used for different parts of a circuit. The layout diagrams indicate where the strips are to be cut. A special tool, called a *spot face cutter* is used for cutting away the copper strip around a hole. You can use a small (e.g. 3mm diameter) drill bit instead, but the proper tool is more convenient to handle.

Usually a row of holes is cut to isolate one integrated circuit (ic) from another and to isolate pins on opposite sides of an ic. Occasionally, where a connection is required between one ic and another, or between pins on opposite sides of an ic, the strip is to be left uncut. Check the layout diagrams carefully to note such instances.

One of the commonest faults in circuit-building is to leave a thin hair of copper bridging a gap that is supposed to have been cut. Often the very edge of the strip remains uncut and bows out around the edge of the hole formed by the cutter. It is then very difficult to see, but it causes a short-circuit that has serious effects on the operation of the circuit. Every cut should be examined using a hand-lens. You may also find that flakes of copper remain on the cut ends of strips and may cause a short-circuit between the cut ends or to adjacent strips.

The components are nearly always mounted on the plain side of the board, their leads being bent if necessary, passed through the holes and soldered to the copper strips (see later). It is preferable not to mount ics directly on to the board, since they are very difficult to remove once soldered in position. Also, it is useful to be able to remove them when a faulty circuit is being checked, or to avoid damaging them by static charges when adding further stages to a circuit. This is why we specify ic sockets for mounting ics.

Other connections on the board are made using insulated wire. For this purpose, single-stranded wire is by far the best; this is sometimes sold under the name of 'bell-wire'. A suitable gauge is 1/0.6 (i.e. one core, 0.6mm diameter).

It is a good idea to buy a few lengths of wire of different colours, as the colouring often helps in sorting out the wiring of a complicated circuit. Multistranded wire (often sold as 'hook-up wire') is not suitable for use on stripboard, as stray strands tend not to pass through the holes, and may lead to short-circuits. Such wire is best for joining terminal pins on the board to off-board components.

There are several ways of mounting the completed circuit board; the method employed often depending on what type of case is being used. Some types of plastic case have slots moulded in the walls and the board just drops into these slots. Before mounting the components, check that the board fits neatly into its slots. If the case lacks slots, you can obtain pcb guides which consist of a plastic strip incorporating a slot, and with a self-adhesive base. These grip the edge of a board firmly and adhere securely to the wall of the case.

Another simple technique, suitable for small boards, is to use a lump of Blu-tack, or a double-sided adhesive pad, such as those sold under the name of 'Sticky Fixers'. Nuts and bolts may be used, and also self-tapping screws. Some cases have internal bosses specially intended for taking such screws. If you are using these, bore suitable holes in the board before commencing construction, taking care to locate the holes so that you do not cut copper strips that are being used as connections, and that the metal bolt and nut do not cause short-circuits between adjacent strips.

It may be necessary to thread spacers or collars on the bolts to hold the board away from the case, especially if the case is made of metal. Alternatively, use nylon nuts and bolts, or mount the board on nylon 'stand-offs'. At one end a stand-off snaps into a hole drilled in the case and at the other it has a peg which fits snugly into a hole drilled into the board.

Soldering
Many people believe that soldering is difficult but, by employing the correct tools and following a few simple rules, it turns out to be surprisingly easy after a little practice. A mains-powered electric iron is best and you will need a mains socket close to your working area.

For stripboard construction, it is essential to have a miniature low-power iron. A 15W or 18W iron is powerful enough and to use one of higher wattage is to risk overheating. The bit of the iron should be cylindrical (not a point), cut obliquely at the tip and not more than 2mm in diameter. A holder for the iron is useful, though some have a hook on the handle by which the iron can safely be suspended beside the workbench. Use multi-core solder-wire, 40% lead and 60% tin, in 22 standard wire gauge.

These are the steps to successfully soldering a joint:

(1) Make sure the two surfaces to be joined are clean; wipe off any grease, and remove any corrosion with abrasive paper.

(2) Switch on the iron and wait for it to heat up. Touch the end of it against the end of the solder-wire; if the solder melts *instantly*, the iron is hot enough. Attempting to solder when the iron is not hot enough can lead to trouble; the join takes longer to make and, during the extra time taken, heat can be conducted to sensitive components and damage them.

(3) Wipe the bit on a damp sponge to remove crusty pieces of old resin.

(4) Touch the iron against the solder-wire and spread a thin layer of solder over the tip of the bit. Add a *little* more solder so that there is *just* enough molten solder on the tip to flow on to the surfaces and make good thermal contact with them.

(5) Holding the iron in one hand, touch the iron against *both* surfaces that are to be joined. With the other hand insert the end of the solder-wire into the crevice between the two surfaces. The solder melts and flows evenly *and easily* over *both* surfaces. Run enough solder into the crevice to obtain a coating of solder on both surfaces (but not so much as to make a large 'blob').

(6) When both surfaces are well wetted with molten solder, remove the iron and the solder-wire and allow the joint to cool. Do not move or disturb the joint until the solder has solidified.

(7) Inspect the joint to check that the solder has flowed evenly on to both surfaces. If the solder has formed drops or beads (like water on a greasy surface) there may be no electrical contact made. This is a 'dry joint'. It can happen if the iron is not hot enough, if it is not pressed closely to both surfaces, or if the surfaces are dirty. If this happens, re-make the joint.

(8) Check the area of board around the joint to make sure that you have not accidentally made hair-like bridges of solder between adjacent copper strips.

The essence of good soldering is a suitably hot iron and a quick easy action — step 5 above should take only 2-3 seconds.

Semiconductor components may become damaged if over-heated during soldering. Use a heat shunt to prevent this. A heat shunt is a spring clip with jaws made of thick copper. It is clipped on to the wire leads of the component between the component itself and the part of the lead that is being soldered. Heat passing along the leads is shunted into the copper jaws, instead of going to the component. Remove the shunt immediately the joint has been soldered.

In several of the projects we deliberately use a blob of solder to connect two adjacent tracks. This is done to simplify the wiring. Check the stripboard layout drawings to ascertain where such blobs should be formed. Melt a blob on each of the two strips then hold the iron in both blobs, running in more solder to bridge the gap.

Some useful tools
In addition to a soldering iron, a junior hacksaw, a spot face cutter and a few assorted small screwdrivers, the following tools are particularly useful:

(a) wire cutter and stripper: it is very difficult and exceedingly time-consuming to manage without a wire stripper; a cheap one is almost as good as the more expensive variety.

(b) a cutter for snipping off wires close to the circuit-board; these help make the board neat and get rid of short wire ends that may subsequently become bent over and make unwanted contacts.

(c) tweezers, for holding small components, inserting wires and a host of other tasks.

Units and values
The following electrical units are used in this book:

Voltage or potential difference: The unit is the volt (V). 1V = 1000 millivolts (mV)

Current: The unit is the *ampere*, more generally known as the *amp* (A). 1A = 1000 milliamps (mA). 1mA = 1000 microamps (μA).

Resistance: the unit is the ohm (Ω). 1000ohms = 1 kilohm (kΩ). 1000k = 1 megohm (MΩ).

Capacitance: the unit is the farad (F), but this is such a large unit that it, or the millifarad, are hardly ever used. 1F = 1000 000 microfarads (μF). 1μF = 1000 nanofarads (nF). 1nF = 1000 picofarads (pF).

Unit shorthand
On the diagrams and sometimes in the text we use a shorthand way of expressing values. In this, the unit symbol is written where a decimal point would normally be written. For voltage we use the symbol 'V'; 5V1 means 5.1V. For resistance we use the symbol 'k' for kilohms, 'M' for megohms, and we use no symbol (or sometimes 'R') for ohms: 5k6 means 5.6 kilohms, 56k means 56 kilohms, 5M6 means 5.6 megohms, 5R6 means 5.6 ohms, 56R or 56 means 56 ohms. For capacitance we use 'μ' for microfarads, 'n' for nanofarads, and 'p' for picofarads: 2μ2 means 2.2 microfarads, 22μ means 22 microfarads, 47n means 47 nanofarads, 820p means 820 picofarads. 100n means 100 nanofarads, though this is sometimes written 0μ1 meaning 0.1 microfarads.

Working voltage
If the potential beween the two plates of a capacitor exceeds a certain maximum, known as the working voltage, the capacitor is likely to break down. For many types of capacitor, such as polyester and polystyrene capacitors, the working voltage is several hundred volts. Their precise working voltage is immaterial in low-voltage projects such as those described in this book.

Electrolytic and tantalum capacitors are made in a range of working voltages, and usually cost more and take up more room on the circuit board if they are rated for a high voltage. Electrolytic capacitors with working voltages of 10V, 16V or 25V are the best suited to these projects. The best are the 10V types, since these are usually the smallest and cheapest. Also it is preferable for an electrolytic capacitor to be operated at a voltage as close as possible below its working voltage. With tantalum bead capacitors the working voltage is usually 10V or 16V, with 25V or 35V for larger-capacitance types. If for any reason you are operating a circuit on, say, 12V instead of the 6V specified in the instructions, check that you do not use capacitors with 10V working voltage.

Handling ics
Most of the ics used in this book are manufactured by CMOS processes. Their main advantage is low current consumption, but one of the problems with CMOS ics is that they are liable to damage by high static voltages. When you walk across a nylon carpet, your body becomes charged to a potential of several hundred or even thousands of volts. If you touch the pins of a CMOS ic the current discharged through the ic may be sufficient to damage the transistors inside. For this reason, CMOS ics need to be handled with care.

In industry, a workstation may be equipped with special conductive mats, and devices to earth the operator and equipment. At home we can not take such extreme precautions but a few simple rules should be followed:

(1) Wear clothing made from natural fibres, such as cotton and wool, to minimise the charge built up when your body and clothes rub together.

(2) Until you need to use them, keep all CMOS ics with their pins embedded in conductive foam or in the metallised cartons in which they are purchased.

(3) If possible, work on a bare metal surface. For example, use the upturned lid of a biscuit 'tin', and wire the lid to earth (e.g. connect it to a cold-water pipe).

(4) Earth your body and tools immediately before handling the ics or the circuit board. The simplest way is to have on the work-bench a table-lamp or other piece of equipment (or the 'tin' lid mentioned above) which has exposed metal that is connected to mains earth. Briefly touch the earthed metal with your fingers or with metal tools from time to time. Discharge from a pointed tool such as a screwdriver or drill is particularly rapid and damaging, so this precaution is an important one.

There are two other rules which you should bear in mind if you are testing partly-completed circuits:

(1) Voltages must never be applied to input terminals unless the power terminals are already connected and the power supply is on.

(2) All input terminals must be connected to something. The ics can not be guaranteed to work properly if there are any unconnected inputs.

Resistors

In the projects, use either 0.25W carbon resistors (5% tolerance) or 0.6W metal film resistors (1% tolerance) unless other types are specified.

Index